Annals of KIRSTENBOSCH Botanic Gardens

Volume 18

J N ELOFF DSc
Editor
Executive Director, National Botanic Gardens

The Way to Kirstenbosch

DONAL P. McCRACKEN

and

EILEEN M. McCRACKEN

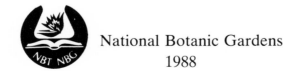

National Botanic Gardens
1988

© National Botanic Gardens

ISBN 0 620 11648 X
ISSN 0 258 3305

Printed by CTP Book Printers, Cape.

BD7782

To the memory

of

Colin and Bessie Webb

The Book and the Authors

Nineteen eighty-eight witnesses the 75th anniversary of the establishment of the National Botanic Gardens centred on Kirstenbosch outside Cape Town. In this three-quarters of a century the institution has grown phenomenally and is now recognized as one of the world's finest group of botanic gardens. This book tells the story of how this was achieved and how successive directors built on each other's work to create one of South Africa's greatest assets.

But the book goes further, delving back into 300 years of the subcontinent's garden history, from the garden established by the Dutch in the 1650s—the *raison d'être* for the original Cape settlement—through to the establishment and growth of a network of colonial botanic gardens in the Victorian era.

The work of numerous curators, such as Auge, MacOwan and Sim as well as others until now long forgotten, is celebrated in this book. The difficulties of climate, penury and even local prejudice made their achievements all the more remarkable. Whether they provided their settlements with economic crops, a scientific depot or just an attractive garden, their endeavours deserve this acknowledgement.

The authors have placed the development of South Africa's botanic gardens in a global context and have thereby endeavoured to contribute to the wider development of garden history, but their primary purpose is to make South Africans aware of this important aspect of their heritage.

Dr Eileen McCracken and Dr Donal McCracken are a mother and son team who have worked together in the past on an aspect of Irish forest history. Dr Eileen McCracken, a retired university lecturer and schoolteacher, has published two major books: *The Irish Woods since Tudor Times* and (with E. C. Nelson) *The Brightest Jewel: A History of the National Botanic Gardens, Glasnevin, Dublin*.

Dr Donal McCracken is a senior lecturer in history at the University of Durban-Westville. He is author of *The Irish Pro-Boers* (forthcoming in 1988) and is directing the Irish in southern Africa project. Currently Dr Eileen McCracken is researching a history of Irish estate and tenant tree-planting, and Dr Donal McCracken is working on a history of botanic gardens in the Victorian British empire.

Contents

Foreword

Botanic gardens have a long history in South Africa, as the old Company Garden in Cape Town was probably the first botanic garden to be established outside Europe, more than 330 years ago. The history of Kirstenbosch (established in 1913) and the other National Botanic Gardens has been recorded by Compton and Rycroft, two previous Directors of the NBG, but no one has yet described the history of the other botanic gardens that were established in the Cape, Natal and Transvaal. In this fascinating account, the authors of *The Way to Kirstenbosch* show how these botanic gardens were founded, how they grew and how they withered through lack of financial support to become shadows of their former glory and not much more than public parks.

Recently books have been written on the history of botanic gardens in Birmingham, Dublin, Edinburgh, Adelaide, Hobart, Sydney, as well as a new one on the history of Kew. This introspection coincides with a re-awakening of botanic gardens to their role in the conservation of plants which are threatened by extinction. More and more people realize that botanic gardens can and should play a very important role in conserving and using plants for the benefit of man.

Botanic gardens are difficult organizations to manage because they must fulfil the frequently conflicting needs of different people. Horticulture, research and education are the pillars on which a botanic garden should stand, but without the anchor of the support of the public, many botanic gardens would cease to exist, as has happened in the past.

The National Botanic Gardens in South Africa have an additional challenge to survive and prosper under changing socio-political circumstances. The authors have shown how attempts are made to face these challenges at Kirstenbosch and the other National Botanic Gardens.

This is the first publication in the Annals of Kirstenbosch Botanic Gardens that is not a botanical or horticultural treatise, but I am sure that it will fulfil an important need and will be enjoyed and used by many students and laymen.

It is fitting that it should be published during the 75th Anniversary of the NBG – an occasion to look back to the origins, but also forward to the future, with the benefit of some of the lessons that the past has illustrated.

J N Eloff
Executive Director
National Botanic Gardens

Preface

Although histories of individual gardens such as Kew have been written during the last hundred years, the study of garden history in general is a recent innovation. A pioneer in this field was the late Miles Hadfield, to whom the authors owe a deep debt of gratitude.

Since 1965 the Garden History Society of Great Britain has done much good work, including the biannual publication of the scholarly journal, *Garden History*. In South Africa, the study of garden history is in its infancy and no collective history of South African gardens has ever been published. This volume is an attempt to rectify this situation at least partially by surveying the history of the botanic gardens in the nineteenth century colonies of the Cape of Good Hope and of Natal and of the institution for which they were the foundation, the National Botanic Gardens of South Africa, which were established in 1913.

The book is divided into three sections: the first deals with the botanic gardens of the Cape Colony. We have included in this section a chapter on the garden of the Dutch East India Company in Cape Town as this was the predecessor of the Cape Town Botanic Garden. We have also devoted a chapter to the Cape public gardens and parks which in the nineteenth century received an annual Government grant. Most of these gardens and parks called themselves botanic gardens at some time during their existence.

The second section looks at the much younger Colony of Natal. Despite the rich flora of Natal and Zululand, because of the Colony's shortage of finance it possessed only two botanic gardens in the nineteenth century. In the concluding chapter of this section we have discussed the contribution these two gardens made to the economic development of Natal. From the point of view of botanical achievement the Natal botanic gardens take precedence over their counterparts in the Cape Colony which often differed little from public pleasure parks. However, because the Cape Town Botanic Garden had such a distant ancestry, predating Natal's botanical institutions, and because there were substantially more botanic gardens in the Cape Colony than in Natal, we have decided that the Cape botanic gardens must be dealt with first in the volume. A concluding section deals with Kirstenbosch itself: its foundation, its role as the National Botanic Gardens of South Africa and the many problems it has had to overcome during the last three-quarters of a century.

In addition to the three major sections we have included an introduction which discusses the general nature of a botanic garden as well as the specific nature of the South African botanical institutions.

We have also looked at the problems facing imperial botanic gardens and stations in the nineteenth century British empire.

Concerning terminology, we have throughout used the word "botanic" rather than "botanical" when referring to the gardens in accordance with general modern usage.

During our research into the subject of botanic gardens we have received encouragement and help from many quarters. We should like to express our particular thanks to Professor Jacobus N. Eloff, Executive Director of the National Botanic Gardens, and the Board of the institution who have given their support to this project and have kindly agreed to publish this volume. Also at Kirstenbosch we must thank Miss Lovell Bosman for her work on our behalf. Thanks are also extended to Dr. Aidan Brady, Director of the National Botanic Gardens, Dublin, who over a period of many years gave us unlimited access to the gardens' library; Professor K. S. Hunt; Mr Brian Schrire of the Botanical Research Institute, Pretoria; Mrs. J. N. Simpson of the Killie Campbell Africana Library, Durban; Mrs. M. Stork, who gave up part of her time while on holiday in Cape Town to consult records in the South African Library; and Professor H. Brian Rycroft, former Director of the National Botanic Gardens.

In addition we should like to record our gratitude to Mr. D. Bain; Mr. J. M. Berning of the Cory Library for Historical Research, Rhodes University; Dr. Peter Brain; Miss I. M. Dugmore, formerly of the Fort Beaufort Museum; Dr. H. C. Hummel; Miss J. Kingwell of the Graaff-Reinet Museum; Mrs. D. Nash of the 1820 Settlers' Museum, Grahamstown; Miss Sophie Olivier, Dr. Howard Phillips; Mrs. K. Plekker; Mr. B. M. Randles and Mr. D. A. Webb of the Kaffrarian Museum, King William's Town; Mr. J. Stark; Mr. Clare Storrar, who consulted material for us in the University of Cape Town's J. N. Jagger Library; Mrs. D. Strutt formerly of the Durban Local History Museum; Mr. Swanepoel of the Uitenhage Museum; Mr. Brian Tarr; Mr. J. Thorns; Mr. E. R. Thorp; Mrs. R. M. Tietz of the McGregor Museum, Kimberley; Dr. W. Tyrrell-Glynn, formerly of the South African Library, Cape Town; Mrs. G. N. Vernon of the East London Museum; and Mr. K. Wyman.

Mention must also be made of the pioneering work done by Mr. R. G. Strey who over a number of years gathered material relating to the history of the Durban Botanic Garden. Our special thanks are due to Mrs Patricia McCracken for her particular skills and expertise in the making of this book.

A garden is an ephemeral thing; the work done by a curator or gardener over a lifetime can easily vanish within a few years of that person's death. While we recognize the truth of Kipling's observation that the glory of the garden "abideth not in words", none the less we hope that we have done something in this volume to ensure that an image is preserved of South Africa's botanic gardens.

Introduction

The primary aim of a botanic garden, as opposed to a park, is to provide practical acquaintance with the plant world. A botanic garden may delight the eye and the aesthetic senses, satisfy idle curiosity and excite wonderment, but the capacity to produce these reactions is of only secondary importance to its basic functions: the accumulation of botanical and horticultural knowledge (research) and the dissemination of that knowledge (information and education).

In a botanic garden the plants are grown in beds which hold some of the species of a particular plant family, and the beds are arranged to show the relationship between one family and another. As it is impossible for even a great botanic garden, such as Kew, to grow every species in a family, it is usual for a herbarium to be attached to the garden. A herbarium is a collection of pressed and dried plants mounted on sheets of paper, each one bearing the plant's Latin name and the date and place of collection. In most gardens, the sheets are stored in special cabinets which are usually housed in a building also called a herbarium.

There are two instances where the arrangement of planting the species of a family together cannot be fully maintained. One is when the family contains both trees and small herbaceous plants, and the other is when some of the plants come from regions with a drastically different climate from that experienced in the botanic garden. The first difficulty is solved by planting the trees in a separate part of the garden called the arboretum or, if they are conifers, the pinetum. The second difficulty is overcome by growing plants from different climatic regions in glass-houses where the temperature and humidity can be controlled.

Whether the plants are grown indoors or outdoors the collection is useless from a scientific point of view if the plants are not labelled. The maintenance of labels is a perennial problem that every botanic garden had—and has—to face. Labels deteriorate, break off, become indecipherable, are rearranged as a practical joke, or are otherwise vandalized. Many sorts of labels have been tried. In the early nineteenth century wooden labels lettered in white paint were used. These were, of course, short-lived: 10 years was a good lifespan for them even in the mild British type of climate and they rotted more quickly in intemperate zones. Some gardens tried terracotta labels, cast-iron labels or china labels. Some gardens gave each plant a number and issued catalogues identifying the numbers. Today the plastic label is widely used.

While the scientific presentation of plant families is the basic requirement of a botanic garden, it carries out other equally important functions in its role as a source of botanical knowledge. It was to the botanic gardens, especially in the nineteenth century, that local people looked for guidance in their choice of crops. In the colonies in particular the botanic gardens carried out research into the various types of crops, fruit trees and forest trees suited to the district. This was a role that was extremely important in South Africa, especially in the eastern Cape.

Kew often acted as a plant testing centre and disseminated suitable plants to various overseas areas. To take a specific example: in 1873 the sheep bush, *Pentzia incana,* a South African plant, was tested at Kew and subsequently seeds were sent to Australia.

From early times beds of herbs were grown by monks and others for medicinal purposes, but what was probably the first garden to merit the title of botanic garden dates from the middle of the sixteenth century when one was laid out at Pisa in northern Italy.

There were famous private collections of exotics in Britain during the same period and the universities of Oxford and Cambridge had their own gardens for the benefit of their medical schools. But in Britain the true botanic garden, as distinct from the herb garden and the university physic garden, dates from the end of the 1750s with the development of Kew out of a garden within a royal demesne. In Britain and Europe most of the important botanic gardens had been formed before the middle of the nineteenth century. Outside Europe, while a few West Indian botanic gardens were established in the last quarter of the eighteenth century, foundation dates lie mostly between 1800 and 1850 [see table 1 below].

TABLE 1: Date of establishment of certain colonial botanic gardens

Bartram (Philadelphia)	*c.* 1730
St. Vincent (Kingstown)	1765
West Bradford (Pennsylvania)	1773
Jamaica	1775
Calcutta	1787
Penang	1796
Martinique	1803
Sydney	1816
Trinidad	1819
Ceylon (Sri Lanka)	1821
Singapore	1822
Wellington	1840
Melbourne	1845
Brisbane	1855
Christchurch	1866
Demerara (British Guinea) and Fiji	1879
Grenada	1886

In the Cape and Natal botanic gardens were set up in the second half of the nineteenth century [see table 2 following].

TABLE 2: Date of establishment of Cape and Natal botanic gardens

Cape Town	1848
Grahamstown	1850
Durban	1851
King William's Town	1865
Graaff-Reinet	1872
Pietermaritzburg	1874
Queenstown	1877

As will be seen, for nearly 50 years subsequent to the British occupation of the Cape there was agitation for the establishment of a botanic garden such as existed in the other colonies. Despite assurances that Cape Town would have one it was not until 1848 that these promises were fulfilled. The Cape Town Botanic Garden, on the site of the old Dutch East India Company Garden, was basically a reconstruction of this older foundation. This phenomenon was not peculiar to the Cape and can be paralleled, for example, by Sydney, remodelled in 1832, and by the St. Vincent garden, remodelled in 1890. In the present century the Trinity College Botanic Garden which had been established in 1806 at Ballsbridge, a southern suburb of Dublin, was removed to a different site during the 1970s.

Although the Grahamstown Botanic Garden was founded in 1850 and the Durban Botanic Garden in 1851, it was not until 14 years later that King William's Town Botanic Garden came into existence. The rest of the Cape gardens, and Pietermaritzburg Botanic Garden in Natal, date from after 1870. As will be seen in the final chapter a botanic garden was founded in Pretoria in 1874.

It is not possible to make an absolute distinction between which of the South Arican gardens were botanic gardens and which were parks because they all had certain common features. They all received government grants which varied between £75 and £650 a year, a sum quite inadequate to maintain even the most modest of gardens, and they had to find the money to help keep themselves running by acting as commercial nurseries. They provided various forms of amusement, such as band performances and promenades, to bring in some revenue. Many of the smaller public gardens and parks had croquet grounds, tennis courts and swimming baths for which an entrance or a hiring fee was charged. At East London and Port Elizabeth there were extensive grassy lawns. Some, after initially styling themselves botanic garden, changed their title to park.

Taking into consideration the harsh environment in which many of the gardens were located, the service they rendered in providing young trees for the surrounding countryside and the streets of the local towns, and the work they carried out in testing the suitability of plants and trees for their area, it would be ungenerous to deny that they performed important tasks, even if they did not lay out beds of families of flowers and label all their plants. Probably only King William's Town Botanic Garden

achieved complete labelling. Indeed, many of the gardens might in a small way be compared to the botanic stations of West Africa and the West Indies whose function was to investigate the economic potential for the area of various plants.

The distribution of plants and seeds from botanic gardens or stations was not confined to Africa. In Australia during the 1860s the Melbourne Botanic Gardens distributed nearly half a million trees which included 40 000 stone pines and 7 000 deodar cedars. Likewise in America the Cambridge Botanic Gardens' arboretum, which was established in 1873, planted out half a million trees in New England. There was a fine dividing line between gardens' offering a service to developing regions and their competing with commercial nurseries. As early as the 1840's, the Peradeniya Botanic Garden in Ceylon (Sri Lanka) was employing a third of its labour force in producing vegetables and fruit for the market in Kandy. Twenty years later the Brisbane Botanic Garden and the Durban Botanic Garden each offered over 60 varieties of plants for distribution in their respective localities. In the 1880s, the Grahamstown garden further supplemented its meagre Government grant by selling bunches of cut flowers for 6d each. James McGibbon, Curator of the Cape Town Botanic Garden from 1850 to 1880, was permitted to augment his salary by the sale of plants.

The *Gardeners' Chronicle* ran a series of five articles in the mid-1850s on the theory and practice of running a successful botanic garden, the first of which dealt with the evils of a botanic garden becoming involved in commercial trading. The writer observed that even if a curator's income depended only partly on the sale of plants, then it was very likely that he would devote greater energy to sales than to promoting his institution in the educational field. The *Chronicle* also claimed that it was not unknown for rare plants that were said to have died to appear later for sale.

The proliferation of botanic gardens from 1800 onwards was on the one hand an expression of the interest in scientific research into better methods of agriculture and horticulture in an age of reforming landlords, and, on the other hand, of the desire to create a living museum for the new plants which colonization and journeys of exploration by plant collectors were discovering in the lands west, east and south of Europe. Indeed, later in the nineteenth century, Sir Joseph Hooker, Director of Kew, commented that botanic gardens were "really to be regarded as an open museum where specimen plants and collections of the greatest possible value are freely displayed".

The full development of botanic gardens, however, had to wait for the technological advances which were made in the first half of the nineteenth century. One of the great problems which botanic gardens had to face was the transport of plants from

TABLE 3: Origin of plants, Dublin Botanic Gardens, 1804

Area of origin	Percentage of species and varieties	Distance from Britain in kilometres (miles)
British Isles	44	
Southern Europe and Mediterranean basin	12,7	3 200 (2 000 miles)
South Africa	12	10 000 (6 000)
North America	10	5 000 (3 000)
Northern Europe	8,3	
Siberia	2,5	8 000 (5 000)
Eastern coast of South America	2,1	
East Indies	1,8	19 000 (12 000)
Australia, New Zealand and Tasmania	1,4	21 000 (13 000)
China and Japan	1,2	24 000 (15 000)
West Indies	1,2	6 400 (4 000)
Jamaica	1,1	6 400 (4 000)
Madeira and Canary Isles	1	1 600 (1 000)
Miscellaneous	1,6	

overseas. It has been calculated that of the plants sent from China only one or two of every thousand reached Europe alive.

Plants were dispatched rooted in containers; they were carried on deck where they were subject to salt spray and unprotected from cold nights; they were kept in the hold where they suffered from slopping bilge water, lack of light, suffocatingly high temperatures in the tropics, mildew and rats. Even the transport of seeds presented difficulties: they were eaten by rats, mildewed, and tended to germinate in the heat and damp of the tropics. Table 3 [above] gives a statistical analysis of the origins of the 6 000 species and varieties in Dublin Botanic Gardens in 1804.

Not unexpectedly, European plants made up two-thirds of the entire collection of species and their varieties. North America and the Cape contributed between them nearly a quarter, leaving only 13% coming from the rest of the world. Furthermore, North America contributed marginally fewer than the Cape, despite the fact that the journey from the Cape was twice the distance of that from North America, and that the voyage from North America was through a zone of temperate climate while that from the Cape passed through the tropics and the doldrums where sailing ships could be becalmed for long periods. The explanation for this high proportion of Cape species in Dublin Botanic Gardens lies in the nature of much of the Cape vegetation. Most of the Cape has not only a low rainfall, but over much of its area the reliability of rainfall, a more important factor than the actual amount, is less than 80%. Many of the Cape genera therefore have to be capable of surviving a low rainfall as well as periods of drought. The extent to which Cape plants have adapted themselves to endure adverse conditions is underlined by comparing the size of the two areas in question. While most of the North American plants came from the states of Virginia and the Carolinas on the American eastern seaboard, the Dublin Botanic Gardens also contained in their figure for this area plants originating from the whole of a continent which stretched from Canada to Mexico. The area of the Cape from which the plants had been collected stretched for only a few hundred miles north and east of Cape Town.

A partial solution to the problem of successful transport of plants came with the invention of the Wardian case in the mid-1830s. Distressed by the fact that the polluted city atmosphere isolated many Londoners from the plant world, Dr Ward devised a container which not only protected the plants in it from an unclean atmosphere, but which also obviated the need for constant watering. His idea was dependent on the recycling of water. A container base was filled with soil, rooted plants were inserted and adequately watered, then a glass top was lowered over the container and its plants. The plants transpired the water as water vapour, which then condensed onto the glass sides and ran down into the earth to be re-used by the plants. Originally the Wardian case was used for house plants, but in the 1840s the invention was applied to the international transport of plants and this necessitated the construction of much larger cases. For example, a case of ferns, some of them seven feet high, was successfully transported from Sydney to Dublin in 1863.

The commercial Wardian case was expensive and consequently was available only to well-established institutions. Since the case was reusable, cases of plants sent to Kew from the colonies were returned to their source filled with European plants: the extent of this traffic is reflected in table 4 [below].

TABLE 4: Wardian cases sent to and dispatched from Kew

Year	Received	Dispatched
1856	21	14
1865	?	36
1871	37	24
1872	33	38

Table 4: (continued)

Year	Received	Dispatched
1873	35	28
1874	23	28
1875	34	66
1876	29	72
1877	31	41
1878	31	?
1879	20	19
1882	28	26

The Wardian case did not, however, provide the complete answer to the problem of plant transport although it was a vast improvement on open containers. The glass top of Wardian cases could be broken and the initial watering of the soil could be either over or under-done. Of 96 varieties of sugar-cane sent to Durban from Mauritius in 1874, for example, only nine varieties arrived alive because the soil in the cases had been over-watered. Five years previously, a consignment of mahogany, cocoa, ebony and 30 other trees sent from Kew to Durban had been destroyed because the glass of the large case had been broken en route. On another occasion Kew rebuked McKen, the Durban Curator, for sending them a case from Natal which had been carelessly packed and contained an insect's nest.

The treatment of plants on board ship was ultimately dependent on the goodwill of the captain, just as it had been before the days of the Wardian case. A Captain Reeves on the India to South Africa run was particularly helpful. In 1887 a consignment of seedling tea plants from the Calcutta Botanic Gardens arrived safely in Durban: "Thanks to the kind attention bestowed upon it during the voyage by Captain Reeves of the *Umvoti* the young plants arrived in excellent condition". Eight years later, when Madras dock officials refused to allow Wardian cases bound for Durban to be stowed as deck cargo, Captain Reeves went so far as to keep the cases in his own cabin at great inconvenience to himself.

Kew made a comparison in 1876 of the efficiency of the two methods of transporting plants. Of 414 plants sent in a Wardian case to Wellington on a voyage lasting nearly four months, 88 died. On the other hand, many of the rooted plants sent in open containers arrived at their destination "sweated and mouldy", rat-eaten and spoiled by bilge water, and of the 100 cuttings of willow species less than 10 plants survived

Avoiding the danger of over or under-watering depended on the skill of the packer, but the problem of glass breakage was less easily overcome. At the beginning of the 1890s the Wire Wove Roofing Company introduced, as an alternative to glass, a web of fine interwoven iron threads which was covered with a thick transparent varnish. This material was tried out by Kew which sent experimental Wardian cases covered with wire mesh to Australia, Ceylon, Jamaica and Lagos. The new covering was favourably reported on although in the tropics the varnish tended to become tacky and any leaves touching the sides might then to stick to them. Wardian cases topped with wire mesh were sent to East Africa in 1896 on a journey of 85 days and of the 34 plants in the cases only six—all mucas—died.

Just as important as the Wardian case was the reduction in the length of time which sea voyages took. While a ship could, under ideal sailing conditions, make the run from Australia to Europe in less than four months it was quite common for the journey to take six to eight months. The change from wooden to iron ships and, more significant, from wind to steam as the ships' motivating power, greatly reduced these times. Distances were drastically cut by the opening of the Suez Canal in 1869 and of the Panama Canal in 1914, for ships from Asia and Australia had hitherto been obliged to go to Europe via the Çape of Good Hope, and those from the west coast of the Americas had had to sail via Cape Horn.

The establishment of an international postal service also aided the successful transmission of parcels of seeds and plants from one part of the world to another. David Moore, the Curator of the Dublin Botanic Gardens, could thus write in 1844:

"Instances have occurred this season of seeds being collected from plants growing at Meerut in India and sent home by overland mail and vegetated in our hot houses within *nine* weeks from the time they were collected."

The railway in Natal conveyed packets of plants for the local botanic gardens free of charge. Furthermore, packets of seeds and plants destined for Kew often went free of charge in the official Government mail bag. In the mid-1870s the Natal Colonial Secretary objected to this. The President of the Natal Agricultural and Horticultural Society responded vigorously, stating that this was a longstanding practice and that the Colonial Secretary should concern himself with the poor spelling of his clerks rather than trying "to teach his grandmother how to suck eggs". The Lieutenant-Governor intervened in the dispute and sanctioned the free transport of small packages in the official mail.

Even with the Wardian cases and the reduced travelling time there were some plant losses. Durban Botanic Garden, for example, sustained losses of between 6% and 46% of overseas plants from 1882 to 1906. On average the loss was 15%. Germination of overseas seeds over the same period was less satisfactory: 32% failed to germinate.

In Britain tropical plants had to be kept in glass-houses heated to particular temperatures. Tropical plants had to be kept in a heated glass-house at the Cape, too, but the gardens there also had the problem of providing shade and lower temperatures for plants from more temperate regions; many of the Cape gardens used open reed-thatched sheds for this purpose. The successful raising of exotics was dependent on technological advances.

Until the early nineteenth century it was not fully realised how much plants needed light; the early glass-houses had solid roofs and often had only one side glazed. These houses were usually built of wood which meant that they had a short lifespan, especially if they were heated. Developments in the techniques of iron making enabled the construction of much larger and longer lasting houses.

The new techniques were employed by Richard Turner, the Dublin ironmaster, at his works in Dublin and London: it was Turner who built, and probably helped design, the Great Palm House at Kew. Another factor which made possible these huge glass and iron structures was the reduction of the tax on glass in 1844. This reduction was so great that the price of sheet glass fell from one shilling and twopence to twopence a foot and a case of crown glass from £12 to 48 shillings. Even so none of the Cape or Natal gardens could afford such lofty glass-houses for the cheapest was over £3 000 (Kew's Great Palm House cost more than £30 000), but some of these gardens did have smaller houses which cost in the region of £1 000.

The cost of a botanic garden consisted of the initial capital outlay followed by not inconsequential annual sums for running expenses. When the Hull Botanic Gardens in England, originally established in 1811, was reconstructed in 1870, it was estimated that £15 000 capital would be needed. A decade later one estimate for the establishment of a botanic garden in New York was US $500 000. Few gardens were as fortunate as that laid out at St Louis in the American state of Missouri in 1890, which was established thanks to a bequest of US $3 000 000 from Henry Shaw. In South Africa a curator was lucky if he received anything more than a grant of land for the founding of a botanic garden, which was often set up with no more finance than its annual allowance.

As far as running expenses were concerned, in Britain in the early nineteenth century it took between £2 000 and £3 000 a year to run a garden, exclusive of the cost of glass-houses and other structures. Within the British empire the annual grant from the government or the municipality varied considerably. In Australia in the 1860s, Brisbane Botanic Gardens received a grant of £1 190 a year, whereas the Melbourne and Adelaide Gardens were more fortunate in each receiving double this amount. On occasions municipalities lent money to gardens, but these sums were rarely recouped. By 1884 the Glasgow Botanic Gardens in Scotland was £40 000 in debt to the Glasgow corporation. Seven years later the corporation recognized the hopeless state of the gardens' finances and took over the institution. The annual Government grants received by the Cape and Natal gardens from their respective governments were on a much smaller scale than those of most of the British gardens, as table 5 [below] shows.

TABLE 5: Government grants and garden expenses, 1881 and 1892 (Amounts given in £)

Gardens/park	Government grant, 1881	Expenses	Government grant, 1892	Expenses
Cape Colony botanic gardens				
Cape Town	650	1 880	500	1 910
Graaff-Reinet	350	910	350	670
Grahamstown	400	2 470	400	2 060
King William's Town	250	770	300	580
Queenstown	100	430	150	630
Sub-total	1 750	6 460	1 700	5 850
Cape Colony public gardens and parks				
Alice	—	—	25	50
Aliwal North	—	—	50	220
Cradock	—	—	100	330
East London	—	—	150	350
Fort Beaufort	25	40	50	50
Humansdorp	25	?	50	80
Kimberley	150	450	300	690
Paarl	—	—	100	120
Port Elizabeth	250	1 610	450	2 020
Riversdale	—	—	75	90
Uitenhage	—	—	75	210
Sub-total	450	2 100	1 425	4 210
CAPE TOTAL	2 200	8 560	3 125	10 060
Natal botanic gardens				
Durban	350	1 070	350	1 400
Pietermaritzburg	350	400	350	500
NATAL TOTAL	700	1 470	700	1 900

The gap between the Government grant and the running expenses demonstrates only too clearly why these gardens became pleasure parks and commercial nurseries. Total subscriptions to a garden rarely exceeded £100 a year, and were usually very much less, and only Port Elizabeth and Kimberley public gardens received a regular grant from the town council. Occasionally East London Botanic Garden was given a municipal grant. The plight of the Cape gardens is paralleled by the Wellington garden in New Zealand. This garden was established in 1869 with a Government grant of £300 a year which was reduced to £100 in 1881, leading Kew to comment that conditions as a result were deplorable.

Apart from lack of funds, the chief problem facing the Cape and Natal gardens was a lack of water. Except perhaps for Grahamstown and Pietermaritzburg, none of them was satisfied with its water supply. Australian gardens suffered in a similar way: in the late 1840s Sydney Botanic Gardens had to be content with a few casks of water a day from the fountain in Hyde Park.

South African gardens fortunately escaped devastating storms, though the Durban gardens suffered some damage during the 1905 floods. This was minimal, however, in comparison with the hurricane which struck the Calcutta Botanic Gardens on 5 October 1864 destroying most of the gardens' 103 hectares (256 acres). One of the finest collections of trees in the east was reduced "to a comparatively naked plain". The Director of the garden noted, "All work since (1796) is gone".

Sir Joseph Hooker at Kew was passionately concerned about the future of the colonial gardens. He considered their true function was to supply Kew with plants and seeds. This was not for the glorification of Kew but rather so that Kew might investigate, propagate and finally dispatch new plants to appropriate destinations all over the world. In Hooker's view Kew should be a plant testing and clearing house for the empire. Hooker deprecated the down-grading of any botanic garden and he was only too well aware of the dangers which threatened them.

In 1877 he wrote:

"Some of the most important functions of a colonial botanic gardens are apt to be lost sight of. Such institutions are obviously likely in most cases sooner or later to develop into the pleasure grounds of the towns and cities near which they are situated. But without disparaging their public usefulness in this respect, it is important that their primary function of promoting the botanical interests of their respective colonies should not be forgotten."

He believed that the curators should be free to make botanical expeditions to obtain plants both for their own gardens and for Kew. If a curator was tied to his garden to make meteorological readings (as Keit was in Durban) then the garden suffered and the policy was in the long run "a short-sighted one".

Not only was Kew intimately concerned with the role of the overseas gardens but it was also an important source of curators, propagators and gardeners for them. In the Cape and Natal the gardens at Cape Town, Durban, Graaff-Reinet, King William's Town, Pietermaritzburg, Port Elizabeth and Queenstown all had Kew-trained or Kew-recommended staff at one time or another. These Kew men were not always a success. King William's Town paid the fare out to South Africa for two: the first stayed for five days then disappeared to the Rand, never to be heard of again, and when the second left after two months the garden's committee was glad to see him go. Another recruiting ground for staff was Scotland. Men trained in the botanic gardens in either Glasgow or Edinburgh or at one of the great Scottish houses were much in demand.

The Victorians believed that if some form of innocuous entertainment were provided for the working classes they would spend their free days—in practice, Sundays—with their families instead of drinking in public houses. Any botanic garden in Britain on which the Government could put pressure by threatening to withdraw its grant was forced to open on Sundays. The Dublin Botanic Gardens, for example, inaugurated Sunday opening in 1861, very much against its will. Kew, encouraged to do so by the Prince Consort, had introduced Sunday opening in 1853. Other gardens which were independent of the Government followed suit. The Belfast Botanic Gardens, which was a private venture, instigated Sunday opening in 1860 but subsequently shut during the hours of evening church services because of "grossly indecent goings-on among the bushes". In Australia the Sydney Botanic Gardens began Sunday opening at the early date of 1839 and Adelaide followed suit in 1857.

There is no doubt but that Sunday opening was popular and stimulated a general increase in the number of visitors. Prior to Sunday opening the annual number of visitors to Kew was 33 000. The year after Sunday opening the number jumped to 100 000 and in 1862 out of a total of 550 000 visitors, 268 000 came on Sundays. In Dublin in the year prior to Sunday opening 39 000 visited the gardens; Sunday opening raised the attendance to 235 000 people.

It is unfortunate that no regular tally was kept of the number of visitors to the Cape and Natal gardens. But when Sunday opening came during the 1870s, the numbers were said to have increased considerably and, as was general in the British gardens, a police constable was usually engaged to patrol the gardens on a Sunday. As in Britain, too, the curators were for the most part able to report that the Sunday crowds did surprisingly little damage.

By the 1880s botanists and other interested people were becoming increasingly aware that the local gardens, admirable as was the role that they played, were completely inadequate to fulfil the functions of a botanic garden in the full sense of the term and to display the rich and unique South African flora. Yet it was to be another generation before the National Botanic Garden of South Africa was established. Even then the new institution had to struggle.

Limited finances and rivalry from the highveld were the main obstacles to Kirstenbosch's development. It is to the credit of the four directors the institution has had that Kirstenbosch has so often been described as the most beautiful botanic garden in the world.

Engraving of Cape Town, c.1763–78, showing the rectangular compartments of the old Company garden.
(Engraving by Tringham after Schumacher, published by J. N. Schneider; Amsterdam: Killie Campbell Africana Library, Durban)

SECTION A: THE CAPE COLONY

1 The mother of South African gardens

The municipal gardens in the heart of Cape Town, between Queen Victoria Street and Government Avenue, is the same age as European settlement in South Africa and was the *raison d'être* for such settlement. The Dutch East India Company, whose ships had been taking on water at the Cape for a long time, had decided to establish a victualling station there to provide fresh meat and vegetables for their scurvy-ridden crews, so when Van Riebeeck landed at Table Bay on 7 April 1652 he was accompanied by an Amsterdam master-gardener, Hendrick Hendricxen Boom. On 1 May, 23 days later, work began on a garden which has survived for nearly three and a half centuries and which has fulfilled different functions at various times.

Priority in planting was given to all sorts of vegetables and herbs. From the bags of seeds which Boom brought with him came crops of cabbages, beetroots, carrots, parsnips, peas, lettuces, onions, artichokes, radishes, cucumbers, horse-radishes, garlic, leeks, cress, sorrel, marjoram, rosemary, hyssop, sage and cereals such as wheat. The first fruits were, naturally, those of a quick-growing kind, like melons and water-melons. The first fruit trees, lemons from St. Helena, were planted in 1654, and two years later 300 apple and other varieties of trees from the same source were put into the garden. Thanks to the encouragement of Nicolaas Witsen, Curator of the Hortus Medicus in Amsterdam, Van Riebeeck cultivated "wild plants of Africa" to ascertain their possible medical properties.

In the face of difficulties—the south-easter blew the plants out of the ground, flood water carried the young seedlings away, cattle broke in and produce was stolen—the master gardener and his slaves gradually established and extended the grounds until the original 5 ha. (12 acres) had increased to 17 ha. (42 acres) by the early 1660s.

In 1657 Boom left the garden, where he had lived in a small reed hut with his wife and children, to farm successfully on his own behalf. He was replaced by Martin Jacobsz of Amsterdam, who in May 1660 was in turn succeeded by Jacob Huybrechtsen van Roosendael from Leiden. Van Roosendael lived for only two years after his appointment. The last master gardener to be appointed by Van Riebeeck was Harman Ernst van Gresnich, a nurseryman from Utrecht who had been at the Cape for six years by the time he was placed in charge of the garden.

In 1679 the first Van der Stel, Simon, became Governor, remaining in the post until 1699. When the Company garden was enclosed in 1679, it measured approximately 1 104 metres (1 200 yards) by 250 metres (275 yards), forming a rectangle covering just under 20 ha. (50 acres). This was larger than the Company garden in Batavia. Simon van der Stel was very interested in the Cape garden. Under his patronage what had been essentially a vegetable and fruit garden in the time of Van Riebeeck now became a garden in a much wider sense. Plants were put in which were desirable not only for their economic importance but also for their intrinsic interest. Van Riebeeck had planted the great central avenue (Government Avenue) with lemons but Van der Stel had them uprooted and replaced by European oaks. It was also during Van der Stel's governorship that the olive trees first bore fruit.

The first alienation of land from the Company's garden took place during the 1670s. In 1677 the lower (or sea-facing) end was set aside for a graveyard, the future site of the Groote Kerk. Two years later a lodge to house the Company's slaves was built, which was eventually replaced in the early nineteenth century by the old Supreme Court. By the end of the seventeenth century, a house for the white gardeners, a hospital, a school, a storehouse and a church had been added at the seaward end of the garden.

Some of the people who visited the Cape at this time left written accounts of the garden. The majority were charmed and pleased. A French Jesuit, Father Guy Tachard, was at the Cape in June 1685 and was enthusiastic about what he saw. "It was remarkable", he wrote, "to find such a curious and beautiful garden in the rather barren country", although the garden did not offer the flower-beds and playing fountains of his motherland.

Peter Kolbe, who was at the Cape from 1705 to 1713, subsequently wrote a long description of the Company Garden in a book he published several years after he had left the Cape. But this account is far from reliable. Likewise the map of the garden given in his book should be taken as only a rough indication of the layout rather than as an accurate delineation. At the town end of the garden the various buildings are shown as lying beside one another in a linear arrangement, for example, whereas this was not in fact so. The Governor's summer-house appears as being about 275 metres (300 yards) long; and while the three longitudinal walks are drawn in their correct positions, only six cross-avenues are included. Furthermore, Kolbe shows the main avenues and the cross-avenues as lined by camphor trees. While there were some camphor trees in the garden they were not the main nor the only species along the walks.

By 1700 the Company garden had more or less attained its final form. It was divided by three avenues, parallel to what is now Queen Victoria Street (New Street until 1900). The central avenue of the garden, which was eventually to be called Government Avenue, was the widest walk at about

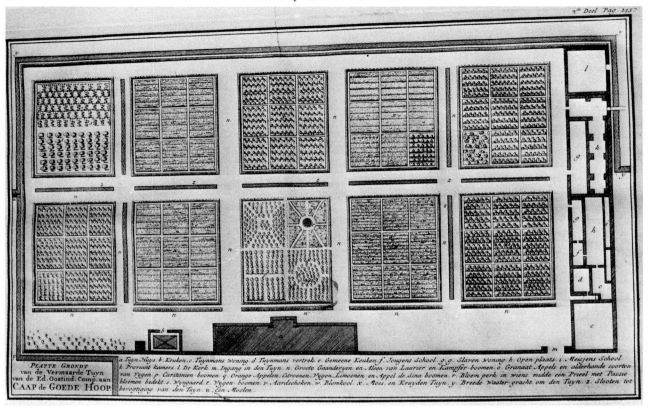

Kolbe's map of the Company garden, published in 1727
(Killie Campbell Africana Library, Durban)

seven metres (24 feet). The avenue on the eastern side, opposite the Governor's summer-house, was about five metres (15 feet) wide but the one next to New Street was wide enough only for two people to walk abreast.

The garden was divided into subgardens by 11 narrow cross-walks and these subgardens were further divided into what were in fact parterres. The central avenue was lined with the oaks Simon van der Stel had planted and parallel to the oaks, on each side of the avenue, was a line of roses far enough away from the trees for a person to walk between the rows. The other avenues were lined with various kinds of trees including lemon, orange, pomegranate, camphor, chestnut (presumably sweet chestnut), "black bark tree", amaquas and "other African trees that please the eye and refresh and divert the sense of smell". The subgardens were protected from the wind by three-metre-high double hedges of "spek", poplars and silver leaf. The smallest divisions, the parterres, were enclosed by hedges of rosemary, sage and hyssop pruned so that "no branch was shooting out and beyond his fellow".

The greater part of the garden was used for vegetables and herbs, but there were subgardens where either fruit trees or flowers were cultivated. At the Table Mountain end were plots of pomegranates, figs, and vines of both European and Persian origin. Little wine was made from them for most of the grapes were eaten as dessert and "still more stolen".

Opposite the Governor's summer-house were chestnut, lemon, orange and shaddock trees and in adjacent parterres a flower-covered mound was crowned with a gazebo over which passion-flower rambled.

A little water-mill at the mountain end of the garden pumped water from a stream which came down from the mountains into the garden's furrows. One furrow, a brick-lined ditch, lay along the side of New Street. Van der Stel had two canals made to run down the central avenue and the avenue in front of the Governor's summer-house so that in the hot summer weather he had a cool and tree-bordered place where he was able to relax and bathe. From these main canals little furrows led to the subgardens. Willem van der Stel, however, was much less interested in the garden than his father had been, and during his governorship the main canals became filled with fallen leaves and slime.

It is not clear whether the garden was completely enclosed by 1700, but there was a brick wall along the New Street side which was 3,6 metres (12 feet) high at the sea end, decreasing in height towards the mountain. To a certain degree this wall also protected the buildings at the town end of the garden. The entrance to the garden was where Adderley Street now becomes Government Avenue, and was controlled by a gate hung between two pilasters. In the 1780s a fine gateway was made with a guard-house on the west side of the entrance.

At the mid-point of the east side of the garden

stood the Governor's summer residence, a two-storey building of stone where the Governor could entertain his friends in the pleasant surroundings of the garden. This summer-house was also used to accommodate visitors whom it was not desirable, for one reason or another, to host at the Castle.

The summer-house was 12 metres (40 feet) long and 5,4 metres (18 feet) wide. The entrance hall was flanked by two rooms paved with tiles, one of which housed a collection of stuffed African animals. A winding staircase led to rooms on either side of an upper hall. Above this was a small loft used for storing seeds, gardeners' tools and dried plants.

Half a century after it was established, the Company garden continued to fulfil its original purpose: the provision of fruit and vegetables for the Company's ships and for the Governor's table. Whether contemporary observers had good or ill to say of the garden, they all agreed that its tree-lined avenues and paths were exceedingly pleasant to walk in or rest in on a hot day.

Simon van der Stel appointed men to be in charge of the Company garden who were more than just the master gardeners that Van Riebeeck had, of necessity, employed. He found men of botanical knowledge and gave them the title of Superintendent. It was these men who raised the garden from being essentially a kitchen garden, and who introduced plants, which they had collected on their expeditions to the interior, which were of interest to botanists rather than to cooks.

Heindrich Bernhard Oldenland was made Superintendent in 1692. This talented Dane was born about 1663 at Lübeck, the son of Hans Oldenland, a postmaster. Oldenland was both a botanist and a physician who, before he came to the Cape, had studied botany at the University of Leiden under Professor Paul Hermann. He arrived at the Cape before 1689, for he took part in an expedition into the Cape hinterland in that year. During his time at the Cape he put together a herbarium which was contained in over a dozen folio volumes. Each plant was accompanied by a Latin description. After his death part at least of his herbarium found its way to London into the hands of James Petiver (*c.* 1658–1718) who was on the staff of the eminent English physician and naturalist, Sir Hans Sloane. Subsequently the Oldenland volumes were incorporated into the Sloane herbarium. But the years which Oldenland had to devote to the Company garden were few, for he died at the end of the seventeenth century, probably in 1697. Linnaeus wrote of him in his *Critica Botanica*, "Oldenland makes known to his own country the rare plants of the Cape of Good Hope where he dies from the change of climate", and he included Oldenland in his roll of Martyrs of Botany. Another author wrote, "he deserved a better fate and a longer life".

After Oldenland's premature death, when little more than 30 years of age, the position of Superintendent was given to a Dutchman, Jan Hartog, who remained in the post until 1715 when he returned to Holland where his brother Willem was Curator of the Leiden Botanic Gardens.

Jan Hartog, a naval cadet in 1691, was commended to Van der Stel by the officials of the Company as having a good knowledge of plants. "You may test him and, having found him able, employ him also". Hartog was probably employed at the garden as an under-gardener for some time before Oldenland's death.

Hartog made several collecting expeditions into the interior and, as his predecessor had done, added many South African plants to the Company garden. Hartog might have done more for the Cape Town garden had he not been required to spend much of his time looking after Van der Stel's private garden. In fact, Hartog came near to dismissal in 1707 for his neglect of the Cape Town garden. It is widely believed that the credit Willem van der Stel received for the South African seeds and plants he introduced to interested botanists in Europe should have gone to Hartog who collected them on his Cape journeys. Hartog's name lives on in the genus *Hartogea* (of the *Celastraceae* family) which Thunberg named for him.

Apart from the fact that by the early years of the eighteenth century there were foreign and native plants in the garden and it was no longer looked on as merely a fruit and vegetable garden, a change had also taken place in its social role. People were now allowed to walk along its shady avenues during the day. This was a far cry from the early days when only high officials and ships' officers were permitted to enter and trespassers could be given 100 lashes and condemned to work for a year for the Company unpaid.

However, some restraints still remained. It was forbidden to touch, injure or pluck any of the plants, or to smoke or drink in the garden, and slaves were in attendance to see that visitors conformed to these rules. A report in 1753 claimed that those persons found misbehaving in the gardens were liable to be shot by gardeners. Some fruit could be picked with the attendants' permission, but as Captain William Dampier related in 1697:

> "If you think to do it clandestinely, you may be mistaken . . . one who took 5 or 6 pomegranates was espied by one of the slaves and threatened to be carried before the Governor; I believe it cost him some money to make his peace, for I heard no more of it".

If one wanted decorations for a wedding, some laurel or rosemary or myrtle say, a couple of bottles of wine slipped to one of the white under-gardeners could produce trimming of the required shrub.

In the mid-eighteenth century Johann Andreas Auge took charge of the garden. Auge was a German, born at Stolberg in 1711, but before he was 20 he had emigrated to Holland where he studied under Boerhaave, and also became acquainted with the collection of Cape plants which Oldenland and others had taken to Europe. Auge came to the Cape in 1747 and was made assistant gardener in the Company garden.

Some time after 1751, but before 1761, he became Superintendent and, according to Lichtenstein, it was Auge who "exerted the utmost diligence to stock the garden with every sort of rare African plant so as to convert it into a true botanic garden". In his search for plants Auge made journeys as far afield as Mauritius. It was Auge's misfortune that the credit for the plants he sent to England was given to others. The last Director of the Cape Town Botanic Garden, Peter MacOwan, said that Auge raised the garden from its original cabbage-growing to something like a botanic garden. It was in 1774, during Auge's time at the garden, that a beautiful avenue of chestnut trees was cut down to provide wood to make furniture for Governor van Plettenberg. In the place of the chestnuts oak trees were planted.

Failing eyesight forced Auge to resign his position as Superintendent in 1778. He retired to the farm of a friend on the banks of the Gamtoos River. Later, after losing his books and collection of plants in an African raid, he was brought to a farm near Swellendam where he was supported by the landdrost, A. A. Faure. When the British occupied the Cape in 1795 they deprived Auge of his small pension. Lichtenstein visited him when he was 93, shortly before his death. He found that Auge . . .

> "still retained all his love for his favourite science. He enquired with very particular interest about the botanic gardens at Cape Town, asking whether such and such trees that he had planted were in a flourishing condition with the same anxiety as if they had been the friends of his youth. 'Is my *Heliconia alba* alive?—is my *Corallodendron* as fine a tree as ever?' He begged me to describe them to him, how tall and thick they were and he said he should die happier if he could but feel them once again . . . I had the pleasure of being the first to tell him that Thunberg had called a species [*sic*] of plant after him, *Augea capensis*, in order that future botanists might have a lasting memorial of his services."

An old *Erythrina caffra* in the garden near the present fence at the museum was probably the tree Auge planted; a group of *Strelitzia alba* in the lower part of the garden was also probably planted by him. Master gardener and botanist, Auge found his final refuge at the farm Rotterdam on the Bullebyaagts River where he is buried near a plantation of poplars and oaks. His name is commemorated in a side road in Swellendam, Augestraat, just off Bergstraat.

Captain Cook visited the garden in 1771, as did the celebrated Joseph Banks who was attached to Cook's ship as botanist. Cook wrote a succinct description of the garden at that time. It was:

> "about two-thirds of an English mile long; the whole is divided by walks, which intersect each other at right angles, and are planted with oaks that are clipt into wall hedges, except the centre walks where they are suffered to grow to their full size, and afford an agreeable shade which is the more welcome, as, except the plantations by the sides of the two canals, there is not a single tree that may serve as a shepherd's bush, within many miles of the town. At the further end of the garden is a menagerie in which there are many birds and beasts that are never seen in Europe."

In 1778 the garden was visited by Jan Splinter Stravorius, a Dutch Rear-Admiral. Although he had little to tell about the garden—he saw it first and foremost as a supplier of fruit and vegetables to passing ships—he does record some changes that had taken place in its layout. It was still the same size as at the beginning of the eighteenth century but the original three long walks had been increased to five. The central avenue was still lined with Van der Stel's oaks, and the other longitudinal walks with chestnuts. Cypress, bay and myrtle lined the sides of the cross-walks.

The menagerie mentioned by Cook had been established three years before his visit and contained wildebeest, antelope, zebra, ostriches, cassowaries and other species. There was also an aviary full of African birds. Between 1803 and 1806, when the Cape was under the Batavian administration, the zoo area was rebuilt. On the left side of Government Avenue were enclosures for birds and herbivores and on the right was the carnivore enclosure. The latter was entered by a gateway adorned with a lioness couchant; an equally lovely gateway led into the bird enclosure. At the same time Government Avenue was extended to pass through the zoo area and give entrance to Orange Street by way of a Chinese bridge over a stream.

By the time of the first British occupation of the Cape the garden had already fallen on hard times and the number of slaves working in it was reduced. In fact, in 1792 the Company was so hard pressed for money that it leased out the garden. In the last years of its administration the Dutch East India Company was more interested in its gardens at Rondebosch and at Newlands than in the city garden, whose only new feature was a sundial erected in 1781.

The first British Governor, Earl Macartney, arrived in May 1797. During a term of office of 18 months he avoided any unnecessary spending of Government money, for it was uncertain whether the British would remain at the Cape. He lived in the Governor's summer-house in the garden. This house, by now over a century old, was, like the garden, in a dilapidated state. It was cramped and dirty and inconvenient. Lady Anne Barnard wrote that Lord Macartney, gout and all, had to hop like a parrot up the nearly perpendicular staircase.

Macartney handed on to his successor, Sir George Yonge, a request from Mr Barrow, the garden's Supervisor, for a replacement for one of his two under-gardeners who had left. Since the War Office in London had instructed Yonge to confine himself to maintaining the garden as he found it and to incur no extra expenditure, at his own expense he found a suitable replacement and brought him out from England.

Yonge took up the matter of the garden's state

with Henry Dundas. The garden, he said, was in decline when the English arrived and now, four years later, was "gone to ruin and decay". The hothouse had irrevocably broken down and the water furrows had fallen in and were choked with debris. Yet the garden could, Yonge was sure, be made into a very valuable adjunct to Kew.

Yonge was able to effect some improvements during his last two years at the Cape, and it seems probable that he paid for some of the work carried out at the garden himself. He had the choked furrows filled in and replaced by one large irrigation channel, he erected a fountain and he constructed a fish-pond. He also had a wall built round the greater part of the garden.

The wall effectively excluded the public and this aroused such resentment and anger that he had to allow people to stroll along the main avenue. As Lady Barnard wrote:

> "For a hundred and fifty years they had enjoyed the privilege of walking under the shade of these oaks—'tis the only public walk of the Cape—and all ranks of people, the women particularly, were furious."

Burchell visited the Cape Town garden in 1810 "expecting to see in it many things worth attention", but he was disappointed. It contained, he wrote, "scarcely anything except vegetables for the table". He mentioned that at the foot of the oaks, "common English oaks", in the main avenue there grew the pretty yellow flowers of *Sparaxis graminea*, "rather like English crocus". The menagerie was still in existence but contained only a wildebeest, some ostriches, a lion, a lioness and a Bengal tiger.

In 1824, soon after Robert Buchanan was appointed Superintendent, the question of the future of the garden was raised again. A Commission of Inquiry into Cape Colony finances recommended that until the greater part of the garden was converted into a proper botanic garden the £200 currently allowed each year for upkeep should not be exceeded. At the same time Bathurst, the Colonial Secretary, decided that retaining the Newlands garden as a country residence for the Governor was an unnecessary expense. He proposed that the Governor should move back to Cape Town and that the Cape Town garden should be reserved for the Governor's sole use. The laying out of a proper botanic garden on part of the garden's site could be considered when the colony was more prosperous. The salary of the Superintendent of the garden was, however, raised from £54 to £72 a year, and that of his white gardener from £45 to £72.

In June 1827, Sir Richard Plasket, Secretary to the Governor, observed that the central avenue was still a public walk and its closure "would cause more dis-satisfaction than the abolition of the public gardens". At the end of the year Lord Goderich, the Colonial Secretary, added his voice to those of people who were uneasy about the discontent which closure might engender. Restoration of the garden

would, he said, be a very acceptable boon to the old colonists. About £1 000 would be needed to set up a botanic garden and £300 a year thereafter for maintenance.

Sir Lowry Cole, Governor at the Cape from 1828 until 1833, gave pledges that a botanic garden would be established on the site of the Government garden, but the years passed and no move was made. At the mountain end of the garden the land once occupied by the zoo was given over to the South African College, and land between the College and the garden was designated for building. The Governor's summer-house was very much enlarged and renamed Government House. A map of the garden in the mid-1840s shows that only about half of the ground was maintained in any sort of order—that was the area around Government House.

A letter to the *Cape Town Mail* in September 1845 graphically describes the state of the once well-maintained Company garden. That part of the garden which was still accessible to the public was in a disgraceful state of abandonment. No one in authority had the slightest interest in restoring what had been a delightful garden. The watercourses were blocked with debris and the paths were so flooded that in places one had to ford them. The writer maintained that the garden should be placed in the care of the Cape Town municipality, for at the time of writing it was a disgrace to the town. This letter gives credence to R. H. Arderne's testimony to a Parliamentary Commission in 1877: that the garden at the end of the 1840s was full of weeds and rubbish.

The *Cape Advertiser* took up the question of the restoration of the former Company garden in the spring of 1845. The garden was in its present state, wrote the editor, because the Cape's previous Governors were content to:

> "see their horses and cows supplied with green forage, their pigs with acorns, their fires with firewood and their pots and pans with cabbages, carrots, peas, leeks and garlic."

Instead of prizing the trees in the garden:

> "that their souls might become wise, they cut them up, trunk, bark, roots and branches, that their pottage might become warm. They sinned not like Gods, but like gluttons . . . [they] sacrificed knowledge to appetite . . . [they] set the onions of Egypt before the manna of Heaven, the food of pigs before the food of angels."

A Superintendent well qualified in botany and able to lay out a botanic garden should be appointed at a salary of between £400 and £500 a year. Under him there should be an experienced head gardener, four gardeners and apprentices. The initial establishment would mean an outlay of £250 for such items as seeds and plants, and thereafter £1 000 a year would be needed for running expenses.

A petition asking for the establishment of a garden was organized at the end of March 1845. The petition was originally concerned to link the laying out of a garden with a request that State assistance be given to the South African College. It was proposed that the Superintendent of the garden should also have the title of Professor and be capable of giving lectures in botany, natural history and chemistry, making the garden part of the South African educational system as well as an instrument of scientific investigation.

This proposed linking of the garden and the college received the support of Sir William Hooker of Kew and of Sir John Herschel, the eminent astronomer and social reformer. At that time the South African College was the property of a body of shareholders; shares in the college were freely bought and sold. It is not surprising that a number of people were opposed to the scheme on ethical grounds and there was particularly strong opposition among the descendants of the original settlers at the Cape. In the event, the clauses relating to the proposed link were dropped. Facilities for signing the amended petition were provided in the public library, the city hall and the commercial hall. The petition was presented to the Governor but it was not until three years had passed that a move was made to establish a botanic garden in Cape Town.

The naturalist and traveller W. J. Burchell visited both the old Company garden and the Kirstenbosch area. He was impressed by the latter but not the former.

2 Cape Town Botanic Garden: difficult beginnings

The Cape Government's delay in setting up the long-promised Cape Town Botanic Garden may have been due to a reluctance to incur extra expenditure during the frontier unrest of the 1840s. It is also possible that the presence of two important gardens to which the public had some access in or near Cape Town reduced, in the Government's eyes, the urgency of establishing a state garden. These private gardens belonged to two immigrants from Europe who had prospered at the Cape: Villet, a Frenchman, and Von Ludwig, a German.

Charles Mathurin Villet was born about 1778 in Santo Domingo in the West Indies. He came to Cape Town in 1803 during the Batavian régime, and died at Green Point on 8 June 1856. Originally a Catholic, Villet joined the Dutch Reformed Church and identified himself with the Dutch-speaking section of the Cape Town community. In Cape Town, Villet first earned his living running a school and as an impresario for a group of French actors.

In 1809 Villet opened a shop in Long Street, selling seeds, both living and stuffed animals and bird skins; a little later he founded a zoo or menagerie at Green Point. These enterprises were very successful. His shop was virtually a museum, and his zoo and garden at Les Champs des Fleurs, Green Point, was a great attraction. When the Cape Town museum was established in 1823 he gave the new institution his rare specimens. By the 1830's his stock of plants, bulbs, seeds, fruit trees, vines, dried specimens and drawings of the Cape flora was so extensive that he was dispatching orders all over the world. A year before Villet's death Dr. Pappe was able to say that Villet's garden contained a better collection of plants, and much more approached what a botanic garden should be, than the Cape Town Botanic Garden.

Von Ludwig, a wealthy businessman, was interested in many aspects of science and was a corresponding member of horticultural societies in London, Massachusetts and Boston. At his house in Kloof Street he laid out an extensive garden on which, it was claimed he spent £17 000. He allowed the public to visit his private garden, but only in accordance with a rigid set of rules. Admission was by tickets issued between 10 a.m. and noon at Von Ludwig's house in St. George's Street and valid for the day of issue only. A small entrance fee was charged. No more than six visitors were allowed in one group; children were excluded; and dogs found in the garden were liable to be destroyed. The Cape Town public had access to the garden on Thursday afternoons only. Visitors to Cape Town had freer access: except on Saturdays, Sundays, Mondays and public holidays they were welcome from 1.30 p.m. to 4 p.m. in winter and for a further hour in summer.

Baron von Ludwig (1784–1847). (F. R. Bradlow).

Any scientist, however, who wished to inspect the plants was admitted on any day, except Saturdays, Sunday afternoons and public holidays, at any time except between noon and 1 p.m. Scientists wishing to collect specimens were expected to ask leave from the Superintendent of the garden. Other people who wanted seeds or plants, cuttings or grafts had to write to the Superintendent and send a servant to collect them before 11 a.m. on Tuesdays and Thursdays.

Von Ludwig was said to have introduced more than 1 600 species or varieties of plants to the Cape. On his death at the end of 1847, when he was 66, many tributes were paid to his devotion to knowledge. One of them declared:

> "Such a man is worthy of all praise anywhere, but here he is invaluable . . . all honour to the man, be he who he may, who cultivates science in the uncongenial soil of South Africa."

In March 1848 Von Ludwig's property, including his garden and its contents, was advertised for sale. Many people thought that his garden should be the basis of the new botanic garden. When Rev. Dr. Adamson approached the Governor, Sir Harry Smith, later that month about a botanic garden he pointed out that the plant stock of Von Ludwig's garden could be obtained on favourable terms and, as it would take two or three years to move the

R. H. Arderne (1802–85), chairman of the botanic garden commission.

was composed of five prominent Cape Town men: Rev. Dr. J. Adamson, R. H. Arderne, John Fairbairn, Dr. L. Pappe and H. E. Rutherfoord. These Commissioners did their best to promote the interests of the garden. They donated money to it and some who had substantial private gardens presented it with free plants. For example, in 1855, H. E. Rutherfoord donated the following to the gardens: *Cincona winterii, Croton tiglium, Theobroma cacao, Cookua punctata, Portlandia coccinea* and *Mitraria coccinea*.

Ralph Henry Arderne, M.L.A., a timber merchant, undertaker and upholsterer, was the Commission's Chairman from the botanic garden's inception until it became municipal property. On one occasion he bought a Norfolk Island pine for £5 from a passing ship. The young tree was planted at the main gate of the garden, and by 1951 was 41 metres (135 feet) in height. The first plants to be sent to South Africa from Kew were despatched to Arderne on 12 July 1849.

Perhaps the most renowned of the Commissioners was Dr. L. Pappe. Born in Hamburg in 1803, Pappe qualified as a medical doctor at Leipzig and in 1831 emigrated to the Cape where he practised for many years. He devoted much of his energy, however, to the study of botany. His enthusiasm for the flora of the Cape and in particular for its trees, on which he published a great deal, was rewarded in 1858 when he was offered, and accepted, the post of Colonial Botanist as well as the first Chair of Botany at the South African College.

The upsurge of protest which greeted the arrival of the convict ship *Neptune* in September 1849 affected the garden. Fairbairn and Rutherfoord tried to get the Commissioners to resign as a body in protest against a Government which could even consider allowing convicts to be dumped at the Cape. Although the rest of the Commissioners were more cautious and said that they would resign if any convicts were landed, Fairbairn and Rutherfoord resigned, being replaced by R. Clarence and J. Ross. Later, however, both Fairbairn and Rutherfoord rejoined the Commission.

A grant of £300 a year was assigned for the upkeep of the garden, plus an amount equal to that given by subscribers. The latter part of this promise was never fulfilled. On 2 May 1848 the Government announced that the part of the Government Garden which lay to the right of Government Avenue, stretching from St. George's Cathedral at the seaward end to a sunken roadway at the mountain end, would be the site of the new botanic garden.

Less than 10 years later, in 1857, the boundaries of the garden were changed. The Government took a portion from the garden at the sea end on which to build a library and a museum and in its place gave the Commissioners six acres at the mountain end of the garden. The new area was divided from the main portion of the garden by a deeply excavated subway

plants to their new home, the sensible thing to do would be to purchase Von Ludwig's property intact.

The proposed botanic garden, Adamson believed, should be established in the old Company garden in Cape Town, where the slave lodge could be used for pupils and as accommodation for the garden's staff. The garden would serve a three-fold purpose: it would be an instrument for scientific inquiry; it would enrich the country by collecting and distributing useful plants capable of being naturalized; and it would provide instruction and training for young men in horticulture and botany.

John Montagu, the Colonial Secretary, advised Adamson that it would be necessary to set up a commission to consider the proposals. At the same time Montagu wrote to P. M. Brink saying that the Government would not consider buying Von Ludwig's house and garden, but that it would like to see a catalogue of the plants which were for sale separately from the estate and would pay half the original purchase price of any plants which were acquired for a botanic garden. In the end, part of the collection was bought by the commissioners for the botanic garden when the plants were sold on 5 and 6 June, realizing in all about £700.

The Government decided that the proposed botanic garden should be run by a permanent Commission composed of Government nominees. The first Commission, nominated on 26 April 1848, over which the Commissioners built a bridge of old ships' timbers. Despite efforts to save what plants they could from the commandeered north-east end, much was lost including hornbeams, oaks, holm oaks, eastern planes and many fruit trees. While the soil in the main part of the garden was of tolerably good quality that of the newly acquired upper end was thin and poor. As further compensation the Government gave £300 to the Commissioners, and supplied unemployed white navvies for a few years to develop the new ground. But it was never possible to bring the area into reasonable condition and for many years this portion of the upper garden was used to convert leaves and sweepings into compost. The garden was at this stage some 10 ha. (25 acres) in extent, about half the size it had been a century earlier. In 1848 the nearly flat ground of the garden, although uncultivated and neglected, contained large trees and a variety of other plants, the legacy of the eighteenth century collectors, Oldenland and Auge.

The first list of subscribers was published before the end of May 1848, by which time just over £600 had been raised. The largest amount, £150, came from the Cape Town municipality, the last money which the municipality was to subscribe to the garden for 50 years. Sir Harry Smith, R. H. Arderne, J. B. Ebden, Von Ludwig's widow, F. H. Hunhardt, Borradailes and Co., and John Ross, the owner of Mount Nelson, each contributed £10, but all the other donations were smaller:

Number of subscribers	Donation each
7	£10
21	£5
49	£2–£5
81	£1
32	under £1

By the time the subscription lists were closed over £800 had been collected, which would have meant the garden benefiting from a further £800 of government money had the Government kept its promise to match the total amount of subscription funds.

The Commissioners were never given the title deeds to the land but, nevertheless, they were held personally responsible for the finances of the garden. By 1850 they found that they were in debt to their bank which refused to cash any more of the Commission's cheques. This debt was partly accounted for by the fact that in 1850 there was no Legislative Council to grant funding to the garden. To tide the garden over this difficult time four of the Commissioners each lent the gardens £100 and they were reimbursed the following year by the Government. The garden, however, remained in debt until 1855.

The first Curator was Thomas Draper who had been in charge of Von Ludwig's garden. Draper began his renovation of the old Company garden by

Dr C. W. L. Pappe (1803–62) was a botanic garden commissioner. Later he became the Cape's Colonial Botanist and the South African College's first professor of botany.

growing potatoes and fodder crops to clean the ground. He also designed a ground plan for the new garden which was said to show great discernment, although James McGibbon, who eventually succeeded Draper, remarked later that "from the manner in which the gardens was laid out and planted it did not appear to have been intended for a botanical garden."

Karl Zeyher, an eminent plant collector, joined the garden's staff at the same time as Draper. Relations between the two were strained. Pappe asserted that Zeyher was continually thwarted by Draper, "an experienced but rather whimsical man" and "an efficient gardener", because he knew little botany and was jealous of Zeyher's knowledge. Zeyher was born in August 1799 at Dillenberg in Germany and had been trained by his uncle, Johann Michael Zeyher, head gardener at the Grand Duke Karl Theodore of Baden's garden at Schwetzinger. The young Zeyher had come to South Africa in his early twenties, so by the time of his appointment he had a quarter of a century's experience of working on the flora of South Africa and Mauritius. For a salary of £90 a year Zeyher was expected to name and label the plants, to collect specimens from the open countryside, to instruct apprentices in theoretical and practical botany, to prepare specimens for the herbarium, to show strangers round the garden and to lay out part of the garden according to de Candolli's classification of plants.

Draper resigned to go to Grahamstown Botanic Garden in 1850 and his place as head gardener was taken by Zeyher. Shortly afterwards Zeyher was dismissed as part of an effort by the indebted Garden's Commission to economize. He was replaced by James McGibbon in March 1850 at a salary of £80 a year. Pappe, disgusted and outraged by the substitution of "an experienced and excellent botanist" by "a messenger in the Portuguese Mixed Commission . . . a mere gardener" resigned as a Commissioner. It is clear that the other Commissioners were not entirely happy with the appointment for, as Arderne admitted 20 years later, McGibbon was given a low salary as they were doubtful about his capabilities. Pappe was also annoyed at the installation of fountains and jets for he believed that the available money should have been spent on the establishment of the garden. He also predicted that the removal of the most scientifically minded and useful man from the garden would lead to the total failure of the establishment as far as science was concerned.

James McGibbon, a practical gardener, remained at the garden until his retirement 30 years later. He was born in 1820 in Elgin in Scotland and was a tall and austere man who, while at the Cape Town Botanic Garden used to prod small boys with a stick if he caught them stealing flowers. In early life he was apprenticed in the Duke of Sutherland's garden and eventually married a daughter of the Duke's bailiff. Her brother was commissioned in a regiment posted to the Cape, where he obtained a job for McGibbon as a messenger to the Mixed Commission Court. Six years after his appointment as Curator McGibbon's salary was raised to £150 and he was given the title of Superintendent in recognition of his competence.

The same year in which Zeyher was dismissed, Dr. Adamson left the Cape for a tour of Britain and America. He used the opportunity to visit botanical institutions and optimistically suggested that the botanic gardens of the northern hemisphere should exchange plants with the Cape Town garden.

At the time of Zeyher's dismissal, Dr. Berthold Steeman was visiting the Cape. Steeman published his impressions of the Cape Town Botanic Garden in the *Journal of Botany*, of which Hooker was Editor. The substance of this article was reprinted in the *Gardeners' Chronicle* of 14 August 1852. The Cape Town Botanic Garden, wrote Steeman, had many plants, two small glass-houses and a library.

"it is now, however, retrograding chiefly through the mismanagement of the commissioners, a body of men, who with few exceptions, seem to be quite incapable of exercising the supreme direction, who . . . have brought not only ridicule upon themselves, but the whole institution."

Their power should be restricted, Steeman believed, to . . .

"mere financial matters and a general control over the whole; and that Mr. Zeyher should be charged with the

chief direction . . . no one was better qualified to fill the part . . . yet he was so situated that he could not attempt any alteration or improvement without meeting strong opposition from both the head gardener and the commissioner."

Steeman recalled how Dr. Pappe had resigned over Zeyher's dismissal with the result that the garden had lost two of "its brightest ornaments". Unless the Government put a scientific person in charge, the Cape Town Botanic Garden "must soon fall to the ground, or, at least, fail to accomplish the object for which it was originally designed."

A second Select Committee, under the chairmanship of F. L. C. Biccard was appointed by the Government in 1856 to investigate the state of the garden. Biccard was the Surgeon-Superintendent of Robben Island as well as being M.L.A. for Cape Town from 1854 to 1858 and a member of the Legislative Council from 1869 until 1872. He resigned as J.P. for Malmesbury in 1877 in protest against the annexation of the Transvaal.

Dr. Pappe was the first to give evidence before the Select Committee. In his opinion, the garden had completely failed to fulfil the functions for which it had been created. There was no attempt in it to make an arrangement based on the classification of plants into various families. The most that had been done in that respect was to group some Iridaceae and some Amaryllidaceae—and even then, instead of the species in each family being placed together, they had been divided into three groups in different parts of the garden. Indeed, one group was under some trees, a totally unsuitable position for plants which belonged to open grasslands. The garden, in Pappe's view, was quite useless as a means of scientific instruction and would continue to be so until a properly trained botanist was put in charge as was the case in European botanic gardens.

The next witness was G. A. J. Heise, a Cape Town apothecary who had learnt his botany in Hamburg Botanic Gardens. He agreed with Dr. Pappe that the Cape Town Botanic Garden lacked any scientific arrangement of its plants and said it was quite useless to his two apprentices in their studies. All the botanic garden needed, Heise suggested, was a coffee house to make it a pleasant tea-garden.

Arderne, as Chairman of the Commission which ran the garden, was understandably more diplomatic in his replies to questions. He pointed out that labelling plants was an expensive business. Most of what he had to say was concerned with an exposition of the garden's finances and he attributed any defect in the garden to lack of money.

Zeyher confirmed Arderne's comments on the expense of labelling plants and when invited by the Chairman to comment on the state of the garden he refused to do so. Rev. G. W. Stegmann testified that the garden was useless and offered "no assistance to the student of botany". It was "a mere pleasure garden". A. Werner said that he had visited all the main botanic gardens in Europe and when asked his opinion of the Cape Town Botanic Garden replied,

> "It is nothing at all: a European gardener would not call it a [botanic] Garden . . . It is only a small pleasure garden".

The memorandum presented by Rev. Stegmann probably summed up the evidence presented to the Committee: "I desire to speak with the highest praise of the garden, such as it is; but cannot award to it the name South African Botanic Gardens".

In June 1856, Biccard as Chairman of the Select Committee, reported on its findings. The Cape Town Botanic Garden, he said, was to be considered a failure in so far as it failed to provide facilities for scientific research or scientific learning. Cape Town's geographical position was such that a proper botanic garden could be "not only the ornament and boast of this city, but acquire a world-wide reputation".

The Committee believed that if the garden was rearranged on scientific lines many who at present went there for pleasure "would stay and learn something of a science which is the source of some of the purest pleasures we enjoy".

Biccard further recommended the appointment of a trained person as Curator to lay out the garden on the basis of the classification of families of plants, prepare a catalogue, form a herbarium and, if possible, give occasional lectures. While the Superintendent of the garden, McGibbon, had zeal and energy, it was considered that he should have to deal with only the financial and general management and act as Secretary. The scientific management should be entrusted to a botanist. As has been seen, the only proposal recommended by the Select Committee to be implemented was an extension of the garden at the mountain end.

One of the most lamentable features of the garden, according to Biccard, was the entire lack of "indigenous productions", a want which should be rectified as soon as possible. When the annual grant for the garden was being discussed in the Cape Legislative Council in 1857, a letter was read from Sir William Hooker in which he pointed out that a very limited selection of Cape plants had been sent to the Paris exhibition. He drew attention to the fact that the Kew collection of Cape plants was currently deficient:

> "I only wish that our noble garden [Kew] had its Cape department proportionally as well filled as it was forty years ago; but that is far from being the case. Our old stock of *Proteaceae, Stapeliae, Mesembryanthema* and succulents, in general, have died off and there is no one to send a fresh supply . . . For what purpose are botanical gardens formed at great expense in our colonies, but to afford assistance by the knowledge and experience of their superintendents in such cases?"

Clearly the Cape Town Botanic Garden was giving little assistance to Kew.

The *Journal of Botany* in April 1857 described the garden as not being in any way:

> "beneficial to the country, and carrying on no correspondence or interchange of plants with the mother country, or with any of the colonial gardens . . . [It is] a mere lounge for the townspeople, attracted thither twice a week, by the presence of a band of music."

To add point to these observations the *Cape Monthly Magazine* in September 1857 published an anonymous article entitled "A Cape Botanical Gardens, as it should be" which opened with the words, "The necessity of the establishment of an efficient and extensive botanical garden at the Cape becomes more urgent every day".

In spite of such pleadings and exhortations to make the Cape Town Botanic Garden an institution of scientific worth, it remained essentially a pleasure garden and a commercial nursery. A good example of the garden's role as a social gathering place may be found in the visit of Prince Alfred to Cape Town in 1862. An "old English fair" was held in the botanic garden and many Capetonians flocked to see the illuminations at night in the grounds, "provided by 3 000 lamps and eight mottoes, which were flashed through the trees by gas jets".

It was unfortunate that there was insufficient money for the upkeep of the garden and that it began its existence burdened by debt, for this led to a trade in seeds and plants. The Commissioners made various arrangements with McGibbon whereby he augmented his salary by sales of plants in a little shop in a corner of the garden.

It is difficult to evaluate the role of the Cape Town Botanic Garden in distributing plants. One major problem facing McGibbon in this activity was that a great many plants, such as fruit trees and conifers, did not grow well in the garden. In 1874 it was noted:

> "Two of the most extensive Cape orders Ericaceae and Proteaceae, which are always desiderata in other countries cannot be kept alive in the atmosphere of the Cape Botanical Garden."

None the less the garden was particularly successful in raising seedlings of Australian acacia, eucalyptus and hakea. By the late 1850s it offered the public the choice of no fewer than 25 varieties of such acacias. McGibbon went so far as to claim that the garden, "called into existence a branch of industry (nurseries) not previously existing at the Cape." The garden certainly provided exotics to help stabilize the sandy Cape Flats in the early 1850s. The following decade the garden was sending out, in addition to timber trees, large numbers of olive and white mulberry plants. By 1868 McGibbon could boast

> "There is hardly a village or district in the colony and in the Free State which does not avail itself of the garden to procure seeds and plants at a moderate price."

The situation of McGibbon running his own nursery in the garden continued until 1876 when at McGibbon's request the Commissioners took over his stock of plants at a valuation, relieved him of all part in the growing of plants for sale, and nearly doubled his salary from £180 to £300 per annum.

How much such sales brought in is not known, but when McGibbon relinquished that part of the garden's function, he was spending about £1 000 a year on seeds and plants, some of which he had imported from overseas nurserymen such as the British firms of Lawsons, Bulls and Low, and Williams and Co., and the Paris firm of Vilmorins.

From the late 1870s onwards the sale of plants brought in about £1 000 to the garden; this revenue reached a peak of £1 310 in 1881. Apart from sales, the garden had two other sources of income, the Government grant and subscriptions from private persons. The initial Government grant of £300 a year had been reduced to £250 during the economic depression of the mid-1860s but was increased to £500 in the early 1870s, at which figure it remained until the gardens ceased to be Government controlled.

The cost of running the garden had increased from about £800 a year in the late 1850s to £1 500 a year in 1880. It was not until the profits from plant sales went to the Commissioners that the garden became free of debt. By then between £300 and £400 a year was spent on seeds and plants and just over £1 000 on salaries and wages.

Subscribers paid £1 for an annual ticket, and until 1859 were entitled to plants from the gardens to the value of their tickets. They also had much freer access to the gardens than had the general public, being entitled to visit the gardens every day except Sundays and able to bring visitors with them. Initially there were about 300 subscribers but the number fell off after 1860, and on average there were about 150 until the 1880s when subscriptions dropped to below 100. This drop was partly accounted for by the expansion of Cape Town's suburbs more than 30 kms (20 miles) beyond the city's boundaries.

In years when a military band played the number of subscribers increased because the general public was not admitted to band performances. But whether or not there were such concerts depended on the whim of the Commander of the regiment currently stationed at the Cape, and in years when there were no concerts the number of subscribers declined dramatically. For example, after a period without band performances, the number of subscribers rose from 35 in 1876 to 146 in 1877 when the band of the 88th Connaught Rangers played in the garden that year. The following year, when there were no concerts, the number of subscribers dropped to 59. Subscribers strenuously objected to gate-crashers on the occasions of band concerts, and wanted police stationed at the entrance gates to turn away intruders.

Until the early 1870s the non-subscribing public was admitted free on two days of the week, Tuesday and Friday, and on public holidays. No records were kept of how many people visited the gardens every year except in the case of "strangers" who had to sign a visitors' book. Their number was in the region of 1 600 a year.

In the early 1870s the Government intimated to the Commissioners that it would like to see the public admitted to the garden on Sundays, as they were at that time to most botanic gardens in the British Isles. This suggestion was opposed by the Commissioners, not on the same grounds as Sunday opening had been opposed in Britain—that is that the crowds would damage the garden—but on the grounds that the number of subscribers would fall if the public had free access on Sundays and hence the garden's income would drop. However, as in Britain, the Government was adamant that there must be Sunday opening. It came in 1875, the gates of the garden being opened at noon. There was, as in Britain, an immediate increase in the number of visitors, very often over a thousand coming on a Sunday. During the 1880s the Commissioners offered to open the garden to the public every day in the week if the municipality would donate £250 a year to the garden. This offer was refused and only when the garden became corporation property was it open to the public throughout the week.

The rules which visitors were expected to observe were clearly stated. Only persons above 10 years old, sober, of decent dress and not accompanied by dogs were admitted. Prams were forbidden entrance. People were not to bring in packages, bags or baskets. This was to prevent picnicking and also to make plant stealing difficult. The garden was a place for agreeable recreation and not a playground so games, running, and jumping over flower-beds were all forbidden. Visitors were expected to refrain from touching plants, and while they were not forbidden to walk on the grass it was expected "that preference will be given to the gravel walks for promenades".

The conduct of adult visitors was for the most part exemplary, apart from some petty thieving towards the end of the nineteenth century. But the Superintendent complained constantly of the behaviour of children "not controlled by the presence of their elders". People, it was alleged, commonly sent young children to play in the garden knowing that they were perfectly safe there and under the mistaken idea that the lawns were for children to play on. The presence of nursemaids seemed to make little difference, for they often romped with their charges, damaging plants and making undesirable noise. Or the maids congregated together under the shade of a tree, gossiping or sleeping while the children did as they pleased. There was also trouble from boys in New Street who broke panes in the conservatories with their catapults.

The provision of seats was not over-generous. To begin with wooden benches were provided and in the early 1860s, when these had rotted, they were replaced by 12 imported cast-iron and teak ones costing just over £2 each. It was not until over 30 years later that more seats were provided: 12 teak seats in the gardens and 25 at the bandstand.

At no period was there a large number of workers in the garden. Initially about a dozen labourers were employed but this number was reduced to six, compared with the 30 to 70 slaves which the Company had used. Occasionally some of the labourers were white, but on the whole the wages offered by the Commissioners were insufficient to attract whites.

The deficiency of skilled labour was a constant problem, especially in the earlier years when the garden had only a small income. Attempts were made to train youths to collect and arrange seeds for exchange with other gardens but they invariably left for better paid work and this task fell on the shoulders of the Superintendent. During the depression of the 1860s the garden could pay labourers only two shillings a day, against the two shillings and six pence given to those in Government employment of a similar kind. However, by 1872 when the grant from Parliament was increased to £500 a year the labourers' wages were between 15 shillings and 18 shillings a week, which compares favourably with the 17 shillings a week being paid to Kew labourers in the early 1870s. As time went by the cost of labour and of salaries tended to consume more and more of the garden's income, rising from about half of total expenditure in the early years to two-thirds towards the end of the century.

Nothing is known about the skilled and the semi-skilled staff until the 1870s. In 1876 Kew sent out a propagator, J. W. Dunston, to the garden. Unfortunately, he was drowned the following year, "an active minded and zealous young man whose prospects were full of promise". When Peter MacOwan was made Director of the garden in 1881 there were, besides a foreman and an assistant gardener: R. Johnston, the head gardener, at a salary of £120 a year; Robert Templeman, who supervised the seed department; and F. Richards, who had charge of the conservatories. Johnston retired in 1881 and was replaced by Henry Chalwin who had just arrived from England. Two years later Templeman was replaced by Edward Hutt, who was in turn succeeded by A. F. Baxter in 1888.

T. W. Bowler's painting entitled, 'The Public Library and Museum from the Botanic Gardens.'
(South African Library)

3 Cape Town Botanic Garden: controversy and change

Twenty-two years after the first Parliamentary Inquiry into the garden's workings, another Select Committee was appointed in 1877 to conduct a similar inquiry. Harry Bolus, giving evidence, said, "I consider [the garden] a great discredit not only to the town but to the colony altogether". It was, he maintained, in quite the wrong situation and had no proper provision for adequate water. Apart from these basic disadvantages it had no proper arrangement (into families of plants), the plants needed to be labelled, the garden was deficient in local African plants and had no proper and regular communications with botanic gardens in other parts of the world. The botanic gardens of the Eastern Cape, Bolus observed, had far more in common with European botanic gardens than had the one in Cape Town. Bolus specified the basic requirements for a successful botanic garden at the Cape:

"(it) should be under government control and be government supported and a colonial botanist should be placed in control of it at a salary of £600 a year—all the botanical gardens in other colonies had botanists at their head."

John Ross, one of the original Commissioners, also testified. He believed that the Cape Town garden was:

"like the parent of the country, and it is through these Gardens that the useful plants are introduced into and disseminated through the country."

The Superintendent should be a botanist, Ross believed, with a salary of more than £300 a year and he should have nothing to do with the sales of plants. Ross pointed out that in Mauritius and in Australia the Government contributed 10 times more to the gardens than the Cape government did.

At Cape Town Botanic Garden, as in British botanic gardens, various types of labels were tried. As a later Curator, Peter MacOwan, pointed out the maintenance and lettering of labels was a fulltime occupation, and in two other botanic gardens with a climate similar to that of the Cape, Adelaide being one of them, a man was employed exclusively for this purpose.

When the Cape Town Botanic Garden had been in existence for a decade it still lacked what the Superintendent called "durable and sightly labels". In response to a plea from McGibbon, the following year, 1858, a few private persons provided the money for the purchase of 250 locally made cast-iron labels which carried the Latin and the popular name of the plant and its country of origin in letters large enough to be legible at three to four metres (10–12 feet).

John Fairbairn later suggested that the necessary information could be printed on a piece of paper enclosed in a cavity covered by glass in an iron frame; 2 500 such labels were imported from England in 1860, having been made especially to specification by Levick and Sherman at a cost of £35. Thus, half of the 5 000 or so plants in the garden now carried their identification. No more labelling was carried out until 20 years later when the use of wooden labels was experimented with. Neither the wooden labels nor the glass-fronted ones proved successful. The sun dried out the oil-painted lettering on the wooden labels; the iron frames of the glass labels expanded in the heat and pulled out the putty, and vandals smashed the glass faces. From the end of the 1890s enamelled labels, with blue letters on a white background, supported on 46-cm-high galvanised iron uprights were used.

Plants which do not thrive in the local climate need an area where climatically suitable conditions can be maintained to suit them. In Cape Town, where the climate is comparable with the Mediterranean regions, artificial climatic conditions must be provided in cool green-houses for plants from the cool temperate lands and in a hothouse for plants from tropical areas. At the beginning of the 1860s, McGibbon began agitating for a heated glass-house. As he pointed out, the purpose of their two glass-houses was to give shade and protection to plants from more temperate lands which were unable to withstand the Cape summer. What was needed was a heated house for tropical exotics. The older of the two temperate houses had been built with a gift of £100 from Sir Harry Smith and an equal amount from private subscribers. This house was described as of "quaint and ornamental design, resembling a bird cage". Subsequent to the erection of this house, but before 1856, a larger temperate glass-house was built.

By the beginning of the 1870s both houses were in a dilapidated state: the "bird cage" was not worth repairing, and in fact three years later it had fallen to pieces, but the larger house would, it was thought, serve for some time if it were painted and renovated.

W. W. Dickson, a public-spirited man who had been a Commissioner since December 1873, offered to contribute £100 towards the cost of a stove-house if the Government would make a special grant of £1 000 for the purpose. Not only did the Government agree to this but it also raised the garden's annual grant from £250 to £500. At the same time a new house for orchids, 9 metres long, 4,2 metres wide and 3,6 metres high (30 × 14 × 12 feet) was built at the lower end of the garden.

The stove-house was erected by Boyd of Paisley, Scotland, in 1875. This was the firm which had constructed the Great Palm House in Dublin Botanic Gardens in 1864. The Cape Town glass-house was built on the ground between the large fountain on the central walk and the bridge which connected the upper and lower parts of the garden. It was cruciform, with a central dome 12 metres high and 7,2 metres wide (40 × 24 feet) and two wings each 9,9 metres long, 6 metres wide and 4,2 metres high (33 × 20 × 14 feet). The glass of the roof and upper walls was painted pale blue to prevent sun-scorch, while climbers provided sufficient shade for the lower parts of the house. The total cost of the structure came to £1 562 which was accounted for as follows: £1 000 to Boyds; freight from England and associated charges, £262; foundations, £125; glazing, £25; labour, £126; granite for the base, £17; and spars for scaffolding, £25. The conservatory was later criticized by MacOwan as being entirely unsuited for a botanic garden and fit only for the grounds of a gentleman's residence. The passages between the pillars were only 0,9 metres (three feet) wide and the front door had no protection so that the south-easterly wind was admitted every time it was opened. What was required was an entrance porch between 2,4 metres (eight feet) and three metres (10 feet) high.

Not only did W. W. Dickson contribute to the cost of the stove-house but he presented the garden with his extensive collections of plants including £600 worth of orchids, as well as ferns and caladia, which completely filled the south wing of the new house. Dickson also sent his gardener at no charge to instruct the garden's staff in the care of his plants for a year. Among other plants placed in the conservatories were medicinal plants and bromeliads which McGibbon brought with him from Kew when he returned from leave in England in 1877. Sir Henry Barkly presented a large collection of Stapeliae (carrion-plants). There was also now a satisfactory home for the plants which were sent from the botanic gardens at Adelaide, Batavia, Brisbane, Calcutta, Melbourne and Sydney and from the Acclimatisation Society of Queensland.

However, as McGibbon pointed out, the plants most frequently asked for by foreign correspondents were heaths and proteas, both of which were impossible to keep alive in the Cape Town Botanic Garden. If adequate returns were to be made to the senders of gifts a fulltime collector would have to be employed.

Despite the acquisition and donation of plants for the stove-house, R. H. Arderne alleged in 1877 that the conservatory was filled up with "common plants to stop it looking naked". Nevertheless, within five years the house was completely filled and surplus palms "and other fine conservatory plants" were sent to Port Elizabeth for the conservatory in the gardens there.

By the beginning of the 1880s Cape Town Botanic Garden had been in existence for over three decades, yet it had failed to become an institution comparable to similar ones in Britain's Australian colonies. This failure stemmed directly from inade-

quate financial support from both the Cape administration and the Cape Town municipality. Insufficient funds led not only to the garden's being starved of adequate facilities, but also to its lacking a trained botanist on its staff. It did, however, bring pleasure to Cape Town people and to casual visitors, some of whom left descriptions of what they found to enjoy there.

A Russian, I. A. Goncharov, visited Cape Town in 1853 and wrote:

> "How delightful the Garden was . . . It was not big—hardly half the size of the Petersburg Summer Garden. I thought of our sumptuous country houses and flower beds where all that we had seen would be under glass or in tubs and hidden away in the winter . . . What a rich collection of dahlias. And here is the *Aloe* family . . . the cactus family is richer than all the others, it occupies a whole lawn. What diversity and what monstrosities and beauties together! I passed many shrubs with bared heads as if they were the letters of a language unknown to me. In the middle of the principal avenue, forming a circle, huge pear trees, just like oaks are growing with big pears almost the size of a man's head, but hard and only fit for stewing."

This circle of pear trees is plainly shown on the 1843 map.

Another visitor in 1853, George Frederick Belcher, recorded his appreciation of Cape Town Botanic Garden after an eight-week sea voyage:

> "I am no botanist, I cannot presume to describe the various new and beautiful plants which I saw—the glass houses protecting thousands of rare and delicate flowers . . . but nevertheless I appreciated all I saw, as much as an ignoramus like myself could be expected to."

At the beginning of the 1860s the French Consul at the Cape, A. Haussman, wrote down his impressions of the garden:

> "Any stranger will find much in the Botanic Gardens wherewith to feast his eyes in the way of rare trees, beautiful flowers and graceful fountains . . . Side by side with the gigantic blue gum tree of Australia rises the magnificent Norfolk Island pine; close to the palm of the tropics, the banana and the traveller's tree droop their long and massive foliage, and the flowers of Europe, the rose, the lily and the tulip, flourish side by side with their South African sisters . . . The arrangement of the shrubberies, its flower beds and its grass plots had obviated as much as possible all inconvenience . . . shady sidewalks in all directions . . Conservatories and one or two good-sized basins filled with aquatic plants produce a very pretty effect."

By the mid-1870s McGibbon was becoming incapacitated by rheumatism in his hands and feet and in 1877 he took eight months' sick leave in England. His disabilities increased and in May 1880 he was asked to resign. He returned to England, hoping to find better health there, and died at Richmond, Surrey, about 1886.

The man appointed to succeed McGibbon was Peter MacOwan. The son of an English clergyman, MacOwan was born at Hull in 1830 and came to South Africa when he was 31. For a while he was principal of Shaw College in Grahamstown and later moved to Gill College in Somerset East where he

Peter MacOwan (1830–1909). In 1903 MacOwan, wearing a grey top hat, showed the American botanist David Fairchild around the garden. Later Fairchild wrote: 'I found Professor MacOwan a charming old gentleman of great dignity and keen sense of humour'.

carried the title of Professor, lecturing in various scientific subjects. At the age of 50 he was appointed Director of the Cape Town Botanic Garden at a salary of £300 a year and at the same time he was made Curator of the Cape Government herbarium. His appointment in 1881 was welcomed at Kew: "With great satisfaction I mention the appointment of MacOwan . . . he has a deservedly high reputation . . . as a South African botanist".

MacOwan had a great mastery of language and was capable of writing incisively. He made use of this ability in his annual reports on the state of the Cape Town Botanic Garden, and to advocate replacing it with a proper botanic garden. The Cape Town Botanic Garden, he wrote, had been established in 1848 on a monopoly of sales (there were then only three or four nurserymen in the Colony) with the bonus of acting as a pleasure garden. Now,

he asserted, it was kept going by the mercantile profits of a seed store. The staff, busied in work that brought in cash, "cannot be spared for work that would bring in knowledge". If the garden raised anything good it had to be sold "and turned into maintenance money instead of being reserved as a permanent attraction". Being tied and bound by a sales system they could not take a proper part in international exchange or, indeed, use half of what was sent to them for many of the interesting plants they received were not saleable. In effect the garden had to find two-thirds of its running costs at its own "pecuniary risk."

The Government revenue had increased 10-fold since 1848 but the grant to the garden had only risen from £300 to £500 a year. Furthermore, the garden had to act as a Department of Agriculture, replying to all sorts of queries and problems concerning the raising of crops—and the Government did not even allow it the postage for these replies. The Government's plantation department at Tokai, outside Cape Town, was providing cheaply produced seedlings and destroying the garden's trade in young trees. The information supplied by the garden on general plant growing was used by the private nurserymen to improve their own stock and consequently there was a fall off in sales from the garden.

In many colonies the Government financed its botanic gardens fully. Melbourne Botanic Gardens, for example, had an income of £6 000 a year, yet its orchid collection was in no way equal to that in the Cape Town Botanic Garden. The necessity of functioning as a commercial nursery did, of course, interfere with the proper business of raising interesting plants and carrying out research work. The lack of money caused the Cape Town Botanic Garden to suffer from other defects, too. The fences and walls which protected the garden from intruders and thieves were in a sorry state. The fruit and vines were all diseased and it was considered that they should all be uprooted and replaced with conifers—the more so as they were only an incentive to petty theft, which was in any case generally on the increase in the garden. It was believed that little could be done to curb this type of theft until a residence for a gardener was built in the grounds.

Another problem was that the paths needed renewing, never having been properly made. Old packing cases from Europe had to be used to patch up dilapidated sheds. The garden had "perhaps the ugliest green-house in South Africa", built to a bad plan with two 46-cm (18-inch) brick pillars to support the roof and with their bases resembling kitchen chimneys. The mountain end of the gardens, beyond the subway, had extremely poor soil and was used only by the college boys as a playground, even though the Commissioners had spent a lot of money on it and it was the source of all olive and mulberry cuttings in the Colony.

A further difficulty was that the Municipality was supposed to allow the garden adequate water supply, but in fact did not do so. The increasing size of plants in the main conservatory posed great problems, too. Whereas in other botanic gardens such increase in size would normally be looked on as a good omen and a token of skilful culture, at the Cape Town Botanic Garden this was regarded with trepidation owing to the difficulty of rehousing plants should they outgrow their present accommodation. Such criticism of the garden was not new, although earlier critics had lacked MacOwan's ability to voice their views in the scathing and well-honed language at his command.

When MacOwan was appointed Superintendent of the Cape Town Botanic Garden he was also appointed Curator of the herbarium, the basis of which was plants collected and mounted by such botanists as William Harvey, Christian Ecklon and Karl Zeyher. The collection had been given to Dr. Ludwig Pappe by Zeyher, and on the former's death the Cape Government had bought it from his widow for £400.

In the mid-1860s the collection went to Ireland on loan to Harvey for use in compiling his *Flora Capensis*. When it was returned to Cape Town the 3 000 specimens were stored in seven cabinets in a room in the Grey Library. Unfortunately by this time the collection had suffered considerably from insects. MacOwan, then in Grahamstown, urged the Cape Governor, Sir Philip Wodehouse, to do something about its preservation. He suggested the collection be sent to Grahamstown to be housed in the Albany Museum. However, instead of acceding to this request, the authorities placed the collection in the hands of James McGibbon. This decision merely served to keep the specimens in Cape Town, for McGibbon did nothing to repair or expand the collection.

For his duties as Curator of the herbarium MacOwan received an additional salary of £100 per annum. This extra governmental expenditure was soon justified for he set about rehabilitating the collection. He was helped in this task by the Governor, Sir Henry Barkly, a keen botanist to whom Sir William Hooker had dedicated the seventy-ninth volume of his *Botanical Magazine* in 1853. Barkly and MacOwan succeeded in extirpating the insect pests and in remounting some of the damaged specimens. MacOwan also doubled the size of the herbarium by adding to it his own collection of dried European plants.

The Cape Government made an annual grant of £150 to the herbarium, a third of the amount allotted to the Cape Town Botanic Garden. With this money, MacOwan was able to increase the number of storage cabinets to 16. Kew helped by sending the herbarium a number of reference books as the nucleus of a library. In 1881 personal help from Britain was given when G. F. Scott Elliot, a botanist attached to Edinburgh University, advised MacOwan on the maintenance and running of an herbarium.

When the Cape Town Botanic Garden was placed in the care of the municipality, MacOwan was appointed Government Botanist and he retained his position as Keeper of the Cape herbarium.

By the early 1900s, when MacOwan had been in charge of the herbarium for two decades, he reported that the original collection had increased 14-fold. The collection of 44 200 specimens was by then made up 57% of Cape plants, 26% European plants, 7% American plants, 7% Australian plants, the remaining 3% being plants from other parts of the globe. These figures compare very favourably with those for the Colonial Herbarium in Durban, which by 1900 had 24 268 specimens, 72% of which were foreign plants and 28% South African.

Very soon after his appointment as Superinten-

Sir Gordon Sprigg's attempt to abolish the botanic garden is featured in this 1889 cartoon. Sprigg, the Cape's premier, is besides the axe. The woman is thought to be Marie Koopmans de Wet.
 The cartoon's caption reads: 'Spoilation of government gardens—the deputation to the premier.
  Oh, Woodman, spare that tree,
  Touch not a single bough
  In youth it sheltered me,
  And I'll protect it now.'

dent, MacOwan had drawn attention to a new problem for the garden created by the growth of Cape Town: the plants deteriorated because they became covered with the dust from the streets. Furthermore, salt water sprayed on the streets to settle this dust was also blown onto their leaves. Significantly, in 1886 when the garden extended over a mere 5,7 ha. (14 acres), he wrote, "The day is coming when the garden must move".

In fact 13 years later, in November 1889, Sir Gordon Sprigg, the Prime Minister, decided to abolish the Cape Town Botanic Garden and to use the ground for the site of a new law court. This was vehemently opposed by Mayor de Vaal and the City Council, Marie Koopmans de Wet and other townspeople. A resolution of disapproval was passed by the City Council and sent to Sprigg. As a result, the felling of trees in the garden was halted and the scheme abandoned.

During the 10 years of his service in the garden MacOwan continually pressed for it to be adequately financed but without any success. Then, in 1892, less than half a century after its foundation, the Cape Town Botanic Garden became municipal property and its title was changed to Cape Town Municipal Garden. Once under the control of the municipality—which had for so long refused to contribute to the upkeep of the garden and had forced it from lack of money into being not much more than a pleasure

garden for the Cape citizenry—improvements were immediately effected.

No repairs had been made to Sir George Yonge's boundary wall until the end of the 1850s, after part of it collapsed. For the next 20 years as the walls further disintegrated they were patched with wooden spars which, since they were quickly pulled out for firewood, had to be constantly replaced. Brick walls were beyond the financial resources of the Commissioners. On his appointment MacOwan declared that the walls were in such a ruinous state that they were beyond repair or patching, and a start was made on stone walls.

At first, stone from the subway's retaining walls was used to replace some of the spar fencing in New Street. Iron railings were erected halfway along Government Avenue and the remaining part of that boundary was fenced "like a kraal". Nothing more was done to the fencing until the Municipality took over the garden. Then the tottering spar fence and cestrum hedge in front of the library were replaced by a low wall topped by iron railings. The fence made of packing cases at the mountain end of the garden made way for iron railings; the old wooden gate was also removed and an iron gate installed. Most of the New Street wall was pulled down and replaced by ornamental iron railings fixed in granite coping on a red brick pointed base.

Again it was not until the Municipality shouldered

the cost that the walks within the garden were properly made. Originally the paths lacked foundations and were simply covered with a scattering of gravel. The Municipality had the paths properly ballasted and surfaced with Claremont gravel. This procedure was greatly facilitated by the loan of a large roller, together with its horse and driver, from the Tramway Company. A 3,6-metre-wide (12 feet) path was laid from Government Avenue to the central walk so that there was now direct access across the gardens to New Street. Along the New Street side, where formerly sale stocks had been grown, a 2,7-metre-wide (nine feet) bed was made and planted with flowering shrubs and annuals. At the same time 23-cm-wide (nine inch) cement gutters were laid along the sides of the walks and edged with salt-glazed tiles.

Provision for an adequate water supply was also undertaken by the Municipality. When the garden was established in 1848 it relied on two wells and on an allowance of 2 300 litres (500 gallons) a day from the city's water supply. Subsequently, its ration was increased to 5 000 litres (1 100 gallons) a day. This extra water was, however, available only during the wet winter months: in the dry summer period the ration was reduced to 4 100 litres (900 gallons) and lack of pressure precluded the use of hoses from the hydrants. Consequently, for three months of the year the labourers had to give six hours out of their 10-hour working day to carrying water—150 cans between 6 a.m. and 9 a.m. and a further 150 cans between 3 p.m. and 6 p.m.

Three other sources of water were available to the garden. There was an old well in the upper part of the garden, the part annexed in 1857, but it tended to run dry in summer, when the garden would resort to supplies from a sluice running down the side of New Street and a water furrow which flowed down Government Avenue. But as houses with gardens were erected in Kloof Street their demands on the stream which fed the New Street sluice very greatly reduced the amount of water reaching New Street and eventually the sluice was covered over. The value of this sluice to the garden had not been very great for it was dry and fetid in the summer and a roaring torrent during the winter rains. The furrow down Government Avenue became useless for irrigation during the 1870s when a public wash-house was established upstream and polluted it with soapy water.

By the end of the 1880s, despite a pump being put on the well in the upper garden, the water supply had become so inadequate that it was difficult to keep plants alive during the dry summer. Once the garden became municipal property an adequate supply of water became available. Two drinking fountains were installed—"a great boon to the public"—to replace the 20-year-old drinking cup attached to a hydrant. What was described as "a new fountain" had been made in the garden's central

A walk in Cape Town Botanic Garden about 1890.
(South African Library)

The garden's fountain at the turn of the century.
(South African Library)

walk in 1856. Forty years later, a fountain which had been erected in Adderley Street to the memory of Rutherfoord, who had actively supported the creation of the botanic garden, was very fittingly moved to just inside the New Street entrance. By this time the 1856 fountain was past repair and was replaced by a white marble one, the gift of Councillor W. Thorne, a local businessman and future Mayor of Cape Town. Thorne's fountain consisted of eight basins inside one large circular basin. Four of the smaller basins were 0,6 metres (two feet) in diameter and the rest were 1,2 metres (four feet) in diameter. These basins were used to grow white and blue waterlilies and other water-loving plants.

Other improvements effected by the Municipality included the clearing of an old rockery, the material being used to build three mounds for indigenous succulents. Old fruit trees were grubbed up and replaced by a rose garden. The conservatory—"so long ugly"—was rebuilt in a more pleasing style and a new 11-metre-long (36 feet) green-house, with teak fittings and stands of Welsh slate, was erected. This new house was for the already extensive orchid collection, which was enlarged and all the orchids repotted with peat and sphagnum moss imported from England. To prevent thefts from this valuable collection the doors of the orchid house were kept locked. The old conservatory, like the rebuilt one, was filled out with teak and slate.

The opening of a chalet with washing and toilet facilities at the town end of New Street on 27 August 1895 supplied a long-felt need of visitors "especially from the country".

The abandonment of any pretence to being a botanic garden was clearly marked by what now became the most important feature of the garden: the displays of chrysanthemums, roses, dahlias and daffodils which drew very large crowds. There were in 1903, for example, 1 700 bulbs representing 12 varieties of daffodils. There would have been more but the imported bulbs were kept at the docks for so long that many bulbs rotted. The chrysanthemums were "a big draw". Five hundred plants of 150 varieties were pruned to between 10 and 50 blooms each. Unfortunately it was in the Cape Town Botanic Garden that chrysanthemum rust first appeared in South Africa.

In keeping with the new concept of the municipal garden's role, cut flowers were supplied for civic functions such as the receptions for Baden Powell, White, Buller, Roberts and Milner after the end of the second Anglo-Boer war.

The former head gardener, H. J. Chalwin, who by 1895 had taken over from Professor MacOwan at the Cape Town Botanic Garden, was now also responsible for De Waal Park, St Andrew's Square, Green Point Park and the plantations on Lion's Hill. Thomas Bourke, the garden's foreman, left to start his own nursery business and was replaced by H. G. Ridley from England. At the same time

J. Mathews, who was Kew-trained, joined the Parks Department staff. He was later to become the Curator at Kirstenbosch. The departure of Bourke illustrates the truth that because the garden was forced into competitive seed and plant trade the men they trained left to set up in business in opposition to the garden.

In 1910 the Union of South Africa was established. By then Ridley had been appointed Curator and the garden was considered "a lung" for Cape Town. The official policy with regard to the garden was to combine "the highest cultivation and presentation of plants and flowers with the greatest comfort and enjoyment for visitors." The collection of 150 species of chrysanthemums invoked enthusiastic praise from Japanese visitors. The extensive collection of orchids in the conservatory, the long pergola which supported climbing plants, the wistaria-covered arch, the myrtle hedge and the water lilies in the recently renovated fountain basin delighted residents and visitors alike. The Boyd glass-house housed a good collection of palms and ferns. The aloes had been removed from their inappropriate position under trees to an unshaded bank. There were beds of ranunculi, anemones and *Celosia pyramidales* flowering in the spring and attractive collections of fuchsias, azaleas, carnations, calceolarias, cinerarias and dahlias on display.

4. Grahamstown

In 1850 some leading Grahamstown citizens set about establishing a botanic garden in their town: this was two years after the reorganisation of the old Company garden in Cape Town into a botanical institution.

If circumstances had been different, the Grahamstown Botanic Garden might have pre-dated the Cape Town Botanic Garden by two years. A garden for Grahamstown was proposed by Rev. W. Shaw and George Jarvis in August 1846, but the idea was opposed by the local magistrate, Hudson. Jarvis and Shaw nevertheless approached the Governor, Sir Harry Smith, who was sympathetic and promised a grant of land and a subscription.

A prospectus was published on 13 July 1850 together with a list of subscribers. Sir Harry Smith, who had indicated his willingness to be the patron of the garden, headed the list of subscribers with his wife, their joint contribution being £25. The Eastern Province bank gave £10, the Frontier and Commercial Bank £5 and 10 people—Dr. W. G. Atherstone, Henry Blaine, William Cock, Robert Godlonton, Robert Jarvie, George Jarvis, Charles Maynard, J. F. Slater, William Roland Thompson and George Wood—each donated £5. Thus the garden was eventually founded with a capital of £90. The contributors also promised an annual subscription of one guinea each.

Renewed clashes on the frontier postponed the implementation of the scheme, and it was not until 1853 that Jarvis, W. R. Thompson and George Wood felt the time had come to press the new Governor, Sir George Cathcart, to carry out his predecessor's promise of a grant of land. Cathcart agreed and Blaine, Maynard, Shaw, Slater, Jarvis, Godlonton and Dr Atherstone were appointed trustees of 2,8 ha. (seven acres) of land lying to the east of Gunfire Hill, and bounded for most of its length by the little Kowie River which separated the area from Beaufort Street. This was considered a very suitable site for the project as it contained part of an old Government garden and was already planted with oaks and other trees. It also had a spring which yielded 900 litres (200 gallons) of water a day. A cottage which still stands in the grounds is believed to have been the cottage used as the garden's office and subsequently as a tea room. It was proclaimed a National Monument in 1984.

During the 1870's a further 0,6 ha. (1,5 acres) were acquired, and in 1885 nearly 24 ha. (60 acres) of unredeemed quit-rent land around Fort Selwyn and on the hill slopes to the south of the garden were added. The new area was planted with *Pinus muricata, P. sinensis, P. sabiana, P. radiata, P. halepensis*, robinia and gleditschia. (When the Department of Nature Conservation took over the garden in the mid-1960s these exotics were clear-felled.)

By the end of the nineteenth century successive grants and purchases of land had increased the garden's area to about 28 ha. (70 acres) so that its boundaries extended from the old provost (a former military lock-up) on the west side, to Grey Street, a continuation of Beaufort Street, on the east and to Fort Selwyn on the south-west. The original entrance was by the road which ran from the west end of High Street through the Drostdy gates. In the mid 1860s iron gates were erected on pillars near the old provost in Lucas Street. After the garden acquired a small strip of land between Grey Street and the Kowie River at a cost of £700, the gates from Lucas Street were moved there in 1877 to make a cart entrance. Finally, in 1885 new carriage gates, 3,3 metres (11 feet) wide, were put up at the Lucas Street entrance. By this time it was possible to drive a carriage the full length of the garden along the main drive which had been edged along the south side with a bank of rough-cut sandstone. From the garden one could continue over Grey Street to the Mountain Drive. People were asked not to drive above a walking pace while in the garden.

Initially, the garden was called the Albany Botanic Garden but within a year or so of its founding it was renamed the Grahamstown Botanic Garden. The aims of the garden were clearly stated: from England, or elsewhere, supplies were to be obtained of the best fruit trees, ornamental trees and shrubs, and seeds of flowers and vegetables needed to improve stock already held in the Eastern Province. The trees and shrubs were to be planted so as to secure a succession of young plants and seeds to be distributed among subscribers to the value of their subscriptions. No pretence of establishing an institution which could provide botanical instruction to the general public was even attempted. For the first few years the Government grant was £150. As in the case of the other botanic gardens, the grant was raised periodically and reached a maximum of £400 in the late 1870s. It was a source of annoyance to the Garden's Committee that their grant was never as large as the one received by the Cape Town Botanic Garden's Commissioners.

The first Curator of the Grahamstown Botanic Garden was Thomas Draper who moved there in October 1855 from the Cape Town Botanic Garden. In 1860 he left Grahamstown and was succeeded by a Mr. Baum. Baum was gone by 1864 and had been replaced by William Tuck. Tuck resigned after staying for only two years. The Garden's Committee had found his work very satisfactory and they regretted his departure. This is not surprising as in the 1890s Kew considered him the most skilful fruit-tree propagator in the Eastern Province.

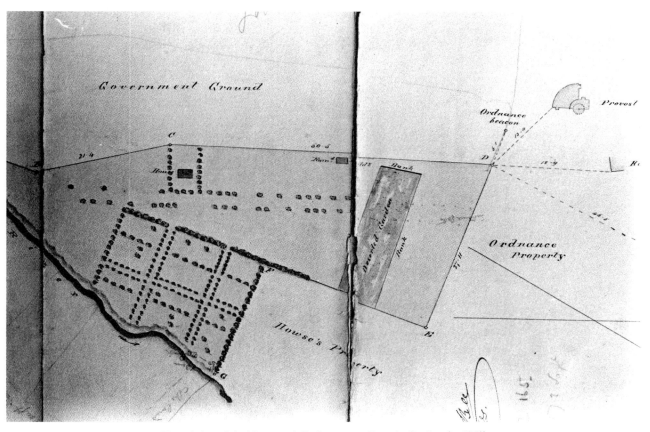

Plan of the original layout of Grahamstown Botanic Garden (*c.* 1850).
(Albany Museum, Grahamstown)

There were three applicants for the position left vacant by Tuck's departure: W. Jardine, C. Webb and Edward Tidmarsh. Jardine was appointed but left the garden in 1868; Tuck returned for a short stint of two years during which time he carried out improvements to the conservatories. Then in 1871 Tidmarsh was appointed Curator. His initial salary was £150 a year plus commission on sales. By the 1880s he was earning £300 a year and a further £150 from sales, so his income was considerably in excess of MacOwan's at the Cape Town Botanic Garden.

Tidmarsh was born in 1831 in Oxfordshire and when appointed Curator he had been living in King William's Town for some time. He remained at the Grahamstown Botanic Garden until his retirement early in 1909; he died in April 1915. While he was in charge, the glass-houses were put up, and he designed and built the first plant fumigator in the district. Tidmarsh was very successful as a propagator and during his curatorship plant sales increased eight-fold. His personal interest was eucalypti, of which he built up a very good private collection. He brought his son, E. M. Tidmarsh, to work in the garden and by 1897 the younger Tidmarsh was in charge of the conservatories. On the outbreak of the second Anglo-Boer War, by which time he was a foreman and clerk of the gardens, E. M. Tidmarsh joined the 1st City Mounted Volunteers, as did C. Rolce, one of the foremen.

The elder Tidmarsh shared with Holly and Paetzold of the Queenstown Botanic Garden the distinction of producing a variety of a plant deemed worthy to feature in the *Gardeners' Chronicle*. During the early 1880s Tidmarsh produced a brilliant scarlet hybrid tacsonia from a supply of seed sent by Baron F. Rothschild. This plant was named *Tacsonia tidmarshii*. The English nursery firm which produced it commercially called it *Tacsonia militaris* and it was under this name that a coloured plate of it was included in the *Gardeners' Chronicle* in 1901.

At the end of the 1870s two staff left to take up curatorships in other gardens: Day went to Queenstown and Davies to Kimberley. Within a few years the garden lost another key man, their Assistant Curator, W. Smith, who returned to England. Smith's place was taken by an Englishman, J. Butters, who specialized in conservatory work. He left the garden after four years. Butters was replaced by two men each of whom held the position of foreman: Robert Palmer was put in charge of the nurseries and Harris looked after the conservatories. Palmer, whose interest was in roses and fruit trees, stayed until he died in November 1897, but Harris left after two years, and in 1891 G. Lockie, newly arrived from England, was appointed in his place. In 1897 Lockie became Curator of the King William's Town garden. When Lockie left Grahamstown, he was succeeded by A. J. Alexander who was made general foreman. At that time, T. Hedges was the plantsman and he was helped by a newcomer from

England, H. Hutchen. On Tidmarsh's retirement A. J. Alexander became Curator.

Throughout the 60 years of its existence as a colonial garden the Grahamstown Botanic Garden functioned primarily as the supplier of trees to the Eastern Cape. It also carried out trials on fruit trees to find the varieties best suited to the district. So preoccupied was the garden with fulfilling the role of a commercial nursery that in 1886 the Government had to write to the Garden's Committee requesting a report on the use to which the parliamentary grant was put. By that time the editor of the local newspaper had already drawn attention to the garden's failure to function as a true botanic garden:

"(It is) simply a cheap purchase of the means of stocking the subscriber's own garden with the most valuable trees and plants and of adorning it with the choicest flowers."

In reply to the Government's inquiry, the Committee reported that the garden was above all concerned with investigating the best methods of cultivation of plants suitable to the local climate. Several young men from England had been trained in the nursery business and "various intelligent" blacks also had been taught "more or less". In fact, most of the budding and grafting was done by blacks. The garden had the best collection of fruit trees in the Cape, and had produced from one blight-free American apple tree a number of grafts for distribution. Over the years the Committee had spent nearly £5 000 on improvements and equipment. The garden was open to the public every day in the year. The Committee also pointed to the existence of a small collection of tropical plants in the glass-houses. The Government was apparently satisfied with the garden's stewardship of public money for no more was heard of the matter.

In the garden's early years, sales of plants, trees and seeds amounted to less than £300 a year but by 1874 such sales exceeded £1 000. In the early 1880s they doubled, and reached their peak of £2 500 in 1893. A combination of four years' drought and the drop in sales during the second Anglo-Boer War reduced the garden's income from plant sales by about a quarter. With the coming of peace in 1902 sales returned to their former level.

The importance of the Grahamstown Botanic Garden as a supplier of trees to the surrounding district should not be under-estimated. Forest and fruit trees were sent to a considerable number of settlements in the Eastern Cape. The German military settlement in the Stutterheim area got all its fruit trees from the garden and many people from Kaffraria and the Orange Free State purchased their plants from Grahamstown. In the 1870s trees were sent to the diamond fields and at the end of the decade, when the gardens carried 45 000 young trees in containers, large numbers of them were exported to Europe. Tidmarsh reported in 1881 that the Port Jackson willows were thriving and were "nice little trees".

The trade in forest trees was stimulated in 1876 by a Government grant towards tree planting, and for the next two decades the garden offered a reasonable selection of conifers and eucalypti. From its early days the emphasis had been on growing these two species. Eucalypti were sometimes sold for as little as one penny each and the garden could offer 40 species and varieties of them. By the end of the century trading in gums had ceased as the Government offered them for sale at an even lower price than that charged by the garden. This did not, however, prevent the garden from continuing to supply seed to nurserymen and seedsmen.

Occasionally the garden worked in conjunction with the Department of Agriculture. In the late 1860s it raised 5 000 mulberry plants from seed supplied by the Government for stock to be distributed in the country districts. In the early 1880s it sold 40 wagon loads of 40 different species of trees to the Forestry Department for planting on the Katberg and a wagon-load of *Cedrus deodara* went to Peri Bush. The *C. deodara* seed sent from Kew flourished in the Grahamstown Botanic Garden though some from India did not.

Fruit trees and roses became increasingly important during and after the 1870s. All types of grafted citrus were for sale and in the early 1890s Seville orange, St. Michael orange, Portuguese orange and lemon were introduced from Europe. To control pests the ladybird was brought from California in 1892. Five years later the garden was distributing pineapple suckers for the Department of Agriculture and even the Cape Town Botanic Garden was buying grafted citrus trees from Grahamstown.

After the second Anglo-Boer War Tidmarsh distributed Smyrna fig and Capri fig for the Department of Agriculture: the Department imported the insect *Blastophagus grossorum* from California to ensure fertilisation of the figs. Sales of roses greatly increased in the mid-1870s and in 1889 a separate rose catalogue was produced. Two years later new varieties of roses were obtained from Europe.

Grahamstown Botanic Garden carried on a considerable exchange of plants with the other South African gardens and, once the garden was well established, with other institutions abroad. The main overseas exchanges were with India, Mauritius, New Zealand and, of course, with Kew. One interesting exchange was made with the nurseryman, A. van Gurst, who on receipt of two cases of zamia from Grahamstown in 1868 sent in return 130 camellias. The Grahamstown curator reported in the early 1880's that some *Encaphalartos frederica guilielmi* sent to Kew some years previously were "the most magnificent objects in the Great Palm House". Likewise, a fine collection of encephalartos sent to Melbourne Botanic Gardens made a very fine show on the lawns.

Grahamstown Botanic Garden was fortunate in that, except in years of drought, it did not have a

Bridge in Grahamstown Botanic Garden.
(Albany Museum, Grahamstown)

water problem. In the early years the garden had three small storage dams as well as its spring. By the mid-1860's there was a pipe from the mains in Beaufort Street and a new well had been sunk in the lower end of the garden. In 1871 the Town Council granted the garden free water-supply from the town reservoir.

The increasing prosperity of the garden enabled the Committee in 1878 to import a steam-pump from England which made irrigation possible over most of the garden. Several local farmers were so impressed by this pump that they bought ones for themselves. New dams were built at the beginning of the 1880s and it was intimated that a new steam-pump would be desirable. However it was not until 1893 that another pump was imported. It had been made by Barley and Co. of Manchester at a cost of £105 and an equal amount of money had to be spent to bring it out to South Africa. The new pump was expensive to use, taking 35 shillings' worth of fuel a day. An extra source of water came at the end of the nineteenth century: the Albany swimming bath took its water from the Slaai Kraal reservoir and the garden used the overflow from the bath. After the peace of Vereeniging a bore was sunk in the garden from which the steam pump could raise 1 400 litres (300 gallons) an hour, and the Town Council installed nine cms (3,5 inch) pipes connected to the town mains.

To honour Colonel Fordyce who fell in the

frontier war of 1850–53, a conservatory was erected in the garden. Subscriptions for this project amounting to £410 were collected and a glass-house was imported from England. Despite the generosity of subscribers, the garden still had to find about £150 towards the total cost. In 1865 a fountain for aquatic plants was installed in the Fordyce Conservatory which was primarily used for cyclamens, calceolarias, primulas, cinerarias and similar flowering plants. The next year a hothouse for orchids was constructed; 10 years later a third glass-house was built; and at the end of the 1880s a stove-house for tropical plants was added to the garden's conservatories. During the 1870s the glass-houses had been covered with wire netting to minimize possible damage from hail storms; however, the glass-houses, especially those with heat, needed constant maintenance. Repairs to all the glass-houses were carried out in 1899 with material taken from the dismantled wood and iron buildings which had housed the Great Exhibition in Grahamstown in December 1898 and January 1899. The garden had been intimately associated with the exhibition, supplying plants for decoration, and Tidmarsh had been responsible for the construction of rustic bridges over the Kowie River which flowed through the site.

The number of subscribers fluctuated and was greater in the years when a military band played in the garden. There were also more subscribers in the garden's early days than later in the century.

Grahamstown people seem to have behaved in an exemplary fashion for there were no complaints about unseemly conduct. The most that Tidmarsh could object to was children causing damage when playing on the lawn in front of the Fordyce Conservatory.

After the end of the second Anglo-Boer War the Grahamstown Botanic Garden suffered a cut in its Government grant, as did the other Cape botanic gardens. Indeed, it was only thanks to J. Slater, M.L.A., who interceded with the Prime Minister on behalf of the garden, that the grant was reduced rather than being completely withdrawn. In consideration of the services which the garden had offered the surrounding countryside for many years in acting as a distribution centre for plants, the Government fixed its yearly grant at £175. The result of the reduced grant was that the garden was forced to rely more than ever on plant sales for its survival.

It was pointed out at the time that the garden, which was of so much benefit to Grahamstown, had never received any help from the Town Council other than free water-supply. This lack of support from the council was compared unfavourably with the support which the local authorities gave to the Port Elizabeth parks. In fact, the Grahamstown Town Council appears to have given help to the garden only once. That was when it donated £50 on the occasion of a garden party given in the garden to honour the visit of the Governor and his wife, Sir Walter and Lady Hely-Hutchinson, in 1910. Elsewhere in Grahamstown, however, there was still interest in the garden. For example, Dr. S. Schonland, Professor of Botany in the newly established Rhodes University College, held his classes on the study of living plants in the garden.

Changes in the status and management of the garden came in 1907 when a new deed of settlement was drawn up and a new Committee appointed. This new Committee of 15 members was to be made up of the Mayor of Grahamstown, the Civil Commissioner for Albany, three life members appointed by the Government, and 10 elected subscribers, of whom five were to retire annually by rotation but were to be eligible for re-election. The Committee could alter or repeal bye-laws relating to the garden but the Government's consent and the consent of two-thirds of the Committee members were necessary to alter the deed of settlement. Significantly, the new Committee was to endeavour to increase the usefulness of the garden by "enlarging the collection of South African flora" and to encourage "botanical and horticultural pursuits". If the garden's resources were insufficient to carry out these aims, revenue was to be increased by raising surplus stock for sale. The account books were to be available to a Government inspector. The final change was the renaming of the gardens the Grahamstown Botanic and Nursery Garden.

Just before 1910 a fourth change was made in the name of the garden: it became the Grahamstown Garden and Eastern Province Nursery. Advertisements were placed under that name in the local press listing plants for sale. After the end of World War I these advertisements also indicated that the garden made a speciality of floral creations for wedding and presentation bouquets, wreaths, crosses and similar arrangements.

The Grahamstown Botanic Garden held out longer than any other Cape botanic garden as a more or less independent institution. It was transferred to the Municipality on 1 August 1922. A further change in status came in the 1960s when additional land was added bringing the area of the garden up to 60 ha. (148 acres), so that it occupied just about two-thirds of the area of Kew. A large part of this addition was, however, given over to the 1820 Settlers' National Monument, an extensive car park and a large area of grass and veld land.

The Government, recognizing that the upkeep of such a large area would put a heavy burden on the Municipality, decided in 1965 to take over the garden and place it in the care of the Cape Provincial Administration. The area was proclaimed a provincial wild flower reserve and the name changed to the Grahamstown Wild Flower Garden.

5 Outlying botanic gardens of the Cape

King William's Town

The establishment of a third botanic garden in the Cape Colony was due in part to the enthusiasm of a local doctor, James Peters, who after a period as a surgeon in the Royal Navy came to Grey Hospital in King William's Town in 1859. Peters was interested in local government and eventually became Mayor of the town. He was also a capable horticulturalist and used his influence to effect the formation of a Committee of trustees to raise money for a local botanic garden. Peters himself assisted the garden with liberal financial contributions when it was established.

Having received a Government grant of land, the trustees laid out the garden in 1865. The Government also made an annual grant of £100 which was augmented by subscriptions of about £100 each year from interested members of the public as well as by plant sales. A green-house costing £50 was paid for by "tickey readings" delivered by the Ven. Archdeacon Kitton. As was general in many botanic gardens in the Cape, regimental bands gave concerts on occasion in the garden.

There are at the entrance to the garden two naval guns, one a 32-pounder and the other a nine-pounder, dating from the late eighteenth century or early nineteenth century. While it is not known how they came to be in King William's Town, their presence in the garden is known to date from at least the early 1870s.

Ten years after its inception the garden was well established. Piped water had been laid on, and thanks to the efforts of Sir Gordon Sprigg and some local men the Government grant had been raised to £250. The Department of Harbours and Railways took as many sapling trees as the garden could raise and the military were helpful in providing any extra labour that was required. Wardian cases arrived from England and were returned filled with South African plants. The Curator, D. Roy, apart from his overall responsibility, was in charge of the vegetable garden: the subscribers expected a steady supply of both vegetables and flowers. J. W. Rowbotham was brought out from England and took charge of the trees, shrubs and flowers.

The annual turnover rose from under £200 in the early days to about £600, with the garden selling £170 worth of plants a year. When drought came in 1877 the lack of water not only killed many of the trees but also adversely affected the demand for plants. However, by the end of the 1870s the drought had ended and the income from sales of fruit trees alone was over £300.

A new Curator, J. C. Nelson, was appointed in August 1879 but he stayed for only a year. Although Nelson's curatorship was of such short duration several improvements were made during his time. The borders, baked dry after not having been dug for five years, were reclaimed and filled with annuals and perennials. A collection of succulents was made, including some donated by MacOwan of the Cape Town Botanic Garden. The area hitherto cultivated as a market garden for vegetables was used to demonstrate trial crops of various agricultural plants and the results were made known to the public, while the loss of income resulting from ending the sale of vegetables was offset by the fees charged for landscaping private gardens.

Further improvements to the garden included clearing out two ponds, a long overdue undertaking since the lower pond had become so obscured by bushes that many of the public were unaware of its existence. The borders of these ponds were planted with bamboo, cella, agapanthus and tree ferns. Seats with backs were installed, and backs were added to the seats already there. Two ornamental iron seats were presented by Geard and Company.

Nelson insisted on the introduction of labels. "A botanic gardens *must* have them," he declared, and he himself made several dozen. On one occasion a convict sent to work in the garden was found to be a skilful letterer so he was set to make such labels as were currently needed and some which might be needed in the future.

Requests for seeds from Calcutta Botanic Gardens, from the Horticultural Society of Madras and from the Acclimatisation Society of Queensland reinforced Nelson's contention that the King William's Town Botanic Garden needed a collection of indigenous trees, if only to make returns for seeds sent to them from abroad.

There were additions to the garden's buildings during Nelson's term of office. A fernery was built which became the favourite winter attraction in the garden and stimulated a demand for ferns in pots. The original glass-house was dilapidated: the staging had collapsed and it contained no plants. A second-hand green-house was acquired for £25 and almost an equal sum was spent in re-erecting it and doubling its size. The new house was filled with a collection of flowering plants as well as plants with attractive foliage, and as a result the public demand for such plants increased. Finally, an office, a heated propagation house, a seed store and a large potting shed were added to form, with the fernery a compact block.

Nelson's successor, James Johnston, also served for only a year. His major concern was the military who gave band performances in the evenings. Johnston complained that the lanterns put up by the military damaged the trees and the audiences walked over the plants. The bandmaster was "difficult". While his band was in the garden, he asserted, that

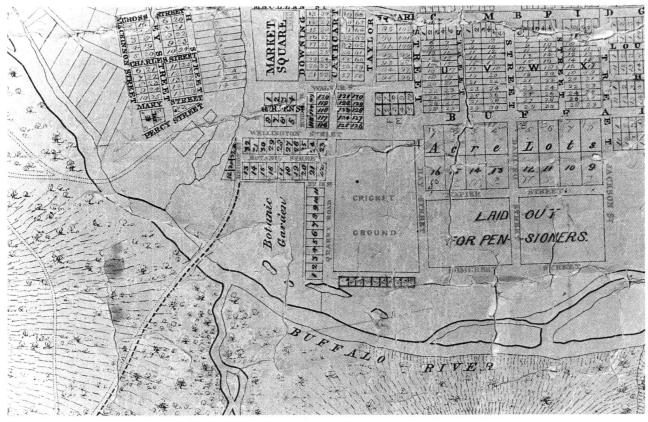

Plan of King William's Town about 1900, showing the botanic garden beside the Buffalo River.
(Kaffrarian Museum, King William's Town)

he was in complete charge of the garden and would brook no interference. Gate money for these concerts came to between £20 and £30 a year, of which a third went to the garden. This amount, however, was not adequate to cover the cost of the damage caused and consequently the evening concerts were discontinued.

The garden was open to the public on Wednesday, Saturday and Sunday afternoons. Sunday visitors, like the visitors to the evening concerts, caused much damage, but Sunday opening was not discontinued.

Johnston was succeeded by James Leighton who remained until 1888. During the six years of his curatorship the garden continued to flourish and, by the time he resigned, annual sales of plants had risen to £700 and free catalogues were being issued. There were 100 000 plants in the 0,8 ha. (two-acre) nursery, mostly shrubs, vines, roses and citrus and other trees. The vines were grown from imported French seed. There was an increased demand for crop seeds: seed sufficient for over 20 ha. (50 acres) of mangel-wurzel was sold every year. The demand for eucalyptus and other trees was so great that an extra £60 worth a year could have been sold had the stock been available. Plant tins for the nursery stock were made locally by contract.

Plots of plants of economic and medicinal value were laid out and a beginning was made in establishing beds of plants according to their place in the natural order of classification. Trees had tin labels nailed to their trunks, and shrubs and herbaceous plants had labels made from oak staves. In fact, of all the Cape botanic gardens, it appears that the one at King William's Town most nearly approached the scientific idea of a botanic garden.

The garden had over 200 species of plants of either medicinal or economic value, and all plants were correctly labelled with Latin and common name and habitat. They included dandelion, sunflower, chicory, tobacco, mullion, foxglove, orache, rhubarb, opium poppy, rape, flax, broom, Chinese tallow tree, caper, indigo, tea, medlar, senna, South Sea Island cotton, pyrethrum, hops, China grass (Ramie fibre), West Indies locust tree and an East Indies grass, Job's tears.

Trials of many types of vegetables were undertaken and the results noted in a book which was available to the public. Trials were also undertaken of various types of fodder crops and of grass, including Italian rye grass, English lawn grasses, seven kinds of maize, sorghum, teosinte—a Guatemalan fodder grass—and prickly comfrey. Connections with Kew were maintained and among the plants which Johnston despatched to Hooker were South African orchids, including species of Polystachyae.

To assist Leighton, the staff was increased. A gardener from Scotland, D. Crawford, was engaged and another gardener, John Young, was put in charge of the nursery. Five labourers were employed at a wage of six shillings a week each and the heavy work was done by convicts. Convict labour was eventually dispensed with since it was found, as in some other gardens, that in the long run, paid labour was cheaper.

The number of visitors to the garden increased with several hundreds coming every Sunday afternoon. Two additions were made to the garden during this successful period. A swimming bath was built and a new conservatory was erected. To finance construction of the bath—which also served as a reservoir for the gardens—a Government loan of £1 400 was secured. The bath was ready for use in 1884. Unfortunately, it was not well patronized: as the locals said, "Why pay money to swim in the bath when one could swim in the river?" Income from admission tickets was less than the £24 wages paid to the attendant at the bath, so three years after it had been built it was let to a Mr George Hay for £50 a year.

A pair of swans was donated to the garden in 1883 by a Mr. Honey of Crayford in Kent, but they were stolen in the following year. Later on Mr. R. Ryan presented three Australian swans but two flew away and one died. The next year, 1897, two more black swans were introduced.

The new conservatory was a memorial to the men who had fallen during the frontier wars. It was begun in 1884 and opened the following year by Colonel F. X. Schermbrucher, who was at the time a Member for the Eastern Province in the Cape Parliament. Originally, this memorial conservatory contained a fountain of polished red Italian granite which had been made to a design by the Principal of Dale College in the town. The excessive humidity caused deterioration in the stone work and it was removed and re-erected in the open air. Eventually the water was disconnected and the bowl used for flowers. The conservatory was paid for with money left over after an obelisk in the town cemetery had been erected by public subscription. Within a few years, however, this memorial conservatory had become a source of anxiety to the Garden's Committee as its fabric needed repairing and it proved impossible to trace who were its trustees.

That was not the only matter for concern: 1888 saw a decline in the garden's fortunes. Sales of plants and seeds dropped by nearly £200, subscriptions and donations fell from £114 in the previous year to £66 and the Curator, James Leighton, resigned. To reduce expenses one of the under-gardeners was dismissed and the money spent on seeds was reduced from £190 a year to £130.

The new Curator, Thomas Robertson Sim, appointed in 1889 at a salary of £200, was a botanist and a forester of some distinction. He had immigrated to South Africa in 1888. Sim was born in Scotland, the son of a farmer and amateur botanist. When young, Sim won the Jubilee Gold Medal presented by the North of Scotland Horticultural Society. He was a fellow of the Royal Horticultural Society and worked at Kew in 1878, then at Harvard

T. R. Sim (1858–1938), the eminent botanist and forester, was curator of the King William's Town Botanic Garden from 1889 to 1894.

Botanic Gardens in 1879 under the eminent American botanist, Asa Gray. While at the King William's Town Botanic Garden, Sim published two books on Kaffrarian ferns and one on Kaffrarian flora. The King William's Town Natural History Association published in 1893 a list prepared by Sim of about 2 430 species found in Kaffraria, with notes indicating the medicinal or economic value of various plants, whether they were trees or smaller plants and which plants had been introduced. Sim won the prize offered by the Prime Minister, Cecil Rhodes, for an essay entitled "Irrigation in the Cape Colony". It was published in the *Cape Illustrated Magazine* in December 1893 and January 1894. Then in 1906 he published his famous *Forests and present flora of the Colony of the Cape of Good Hope*. This book of 361 pages dealt with 312 species and contained 160 plates drawn by himself.

It was Sim's opinion that until botany was taught in the schools the importance of botanic gardens would not be understood. He was successful in getting the subject introduced into Dale College in 1893 and he himself took the boys twice a week for lessons in botany, sometimes in the College and sometimes in the garden. In 1893 six of his eight students passed botany in the public examination and one came first in the Colony.

Probably because of the rigid economies being practised the garden began to deteriorate. The bridges over the stream were "ready to collapse", as

Conservatory in King William's Town Botanic Garden.
(Kaffrarian Museum, King William's Town: South African Railways)

was the swimming bath. The conservatories were in a state of decay and most of the trees and shrubs were sold to defray expenses. Sim reported with regret that the good work the garden was doing in investigating and distributing new and rare plants had ceased as this work had been taken over by the Department of Agriculture. However, the garden still had a stock of ladybird beetles for distributing to farmers in the fight against prickly pear. The one positive achievement at this unhappy time was the acquisition of a new conservatory. A former Mayor of King William's Town, T. N. Dyer, donated a conservatory to the gardens in 1893. It was built in Wimbledon, England, and imported in sections. The 9-metre-long and 5,4-metre-wide (30 × 18 feet) house had a span roof and was heated by hot water pipes. It cost Dyer just over £900.

The Garden's Committee had tried in vain to get the Town Council to give it an annual grant of £150. Two public meetings were called to consider the future of the garden and it was made clear that the public did not wish it to be closed. On 7 August 1894 the garden was taken over by the Town Council. To pay off the garden's creditors the council negotiated a loan of £2 484, repayable over 30 years at £81 a year.

Under the new dispensation steps were taken to rehabilitate the garden. A new bridge of wood and stone was built, the decayed conservatories were repaired, a fumigating chamber was put up and on the south side new entrance gates were erected. The paths were re-gravelled with ironstone, and a new lawn mower was imported from England. The old 5 cm (two-inch) main water pipes were replaced by 7,5 cm (three-inch) ones and water distribution pipes were laid on to taps. As an additional amenity, bands gave concerts "amid fairy lights and Chinese lanterns"; one concert earning enough to pay for 12 new seats. The swimming bath, which had been such a drain on the garden's financial resources, began to be fairly well patronized although it still did not pay its way. Part of the garden which had been leased out was reabsorbed and 1 000 catalogues of the garden's plants were printed.

When the Town Council took over the garden in 1894, Sim resigned as Curator to join the local forestry service; he subsequently became Conservator of Forests in Natal. His successor, T. Wilson, who received only three-quarters of the salary which Sim had enjoyed, died on 10 August 1897. His place was taken by George Lockie from the Grahamstown Botanic Garden and a Mr Henderson was brought out from Glasgow Botanic Gardens as Assistant Curator. During Lockie's curatorship R. Greenfield was in charge of the conservatories and W. L. Oostung looked after the nursery. On his death in 1900, Oostung was replaced by J. P. Sarre, newly arrived from Guernsey. He stayed only a year; his place in the garden was taken by H. G. Field, an English immigrant.

Graaff-Reinet

The idea of making a botanic garden at Graaff-Reinet was first mooted in 1861, but not until 11 years later did the intention become a reality. In October 1872, 40 townspeople signed a petition to the Government asking that a 2,8 ha. (seven-acre) erf next to Willow Walk belonging to a man called Peake and currently for sale should be acquired for a botanic garden. This erf had the important asset of having irrigation water allotted to it. The Government acceded to the request and made a grant to the newly formed Garden's Committee; this grant of £150 a year was raised to £250 in 1876 and to £350 in 1881. By the end of the 1880s 10 ha. (25 acres) were under cultivation.

The site of the garden lay along the side of the Sundays River and was separated from it by a belt of thorn bush which covered five acres. Eventually a walk was made through this bush. Beyond the river, a ridge rose from 150 to 300 metres (500 to 1 000 feet) and gave some, but not complete, shelter from the north and north-west winds.

A Committee to run the garden was appointed in November 1872. The members were Harry Bolus, J. H. Cloete, J. S. Gates, John Hunter McLea, and Rev. Charles Murray, with H. Hudson as Chairman and A. Hartzenberg as Treasurer. Bolus and McLea resigned the following year, the former to go to Cape Town after the death of his wife and son and the latter to the Transvaal. The Committee tried to get William Tuck of the Grahamstown Botanic Garden to come as Curator but he refused and a Mr. Kirschhof was appointed. However, in 1875, J. H. McLea returned from the Transvaal and was made Curator by popular request, with the respectable salary of £200 a year plus half the proceeds of plant sales and a guarantee of at least three years' employment. McLea died in 1878 from a stroke which he suffered while working in the garden.

This time Tuck accepted the post of Curator when it was offered to him. He stayed for only two years, resigning on the grounds of ill-health. He in turn was succeeded by John C. Smith who remained until 1900, when his place was taken by C. J. Howlett, a Kew-trained man from Uitenhage.

A feature of the Graaff-Reinet Botanic Garden was the scroll-shaped beds cut out of the lawns and containing choice conifers; common pines were used as nurse plants and subsequently removed. Other plants for which the garden was noted included peonies, amaryllis, Japanese orchids, carnations, chrysanthemums, tulips and lilies.

Initially water was found at a depth of 8 metres (26 feet): an Essex windmill raised 4 100 litres (900 gallons) a day. The water was used in fountains then run into a pond 1,5 metre deep and nine metres in diameter (5 × 30 feet) where it was available for hand watering. This pond was made into an amenity feature surrounded by a 0,6-metre-high (two foot) wall with ogee coping and pierced with corniced

In the Botanical Gardens.

Graaff-Reinet.

The fountain in Graaff-Reinet Botanic Garden about 1909.
(East London Museum)

pillars to hold flower urns. Steps led up to the pond from the four points of the compass. In the early days the garden needed just over 37 000 litres (8 000 gallons) of water a day from August to March. During the rest of the year a flow of 900 litres (200 gallons) an hour, costing one shilling, was bought from local vine-growers. A Stover windmill installed in 1881 raised 2 300 litres (500 gallons) an hour and served the garden for 16 years. When the Essex windmill was smashed by a 27-metre high (90-foot) blue gum blown down in a January gale in 1892, it was replaced by another Stover. The next year a drinking fountain was optimistically installed, but drought constantly took its toll in the garden and in the first few years caused loss of sales valued at nearly £200.

Disastrous hail storms and frost severely damaged the garden in 1880, 1881, 1886 and 1888. The storm of March 1886 uprooted a 15-metre high (50-foot) *Pinus radiata* and 40 panes in the garden's modest hothouse were smashed. Forty well-grown gums and cypresses were also uprooted and many of the roses were destroyed. The following July, 31 cms (12 inches) of snow disfigured and broke 150 trees. An October frost injured the vines and other young plants, and in November a hail storm so damaged the ripening fruit that none was left perfect. Frost in July 1888 killed many plants and wreaked much damage on the orange groves in the district.

From the beginning, the garden was committed to the supply of vines and trees, especially fruit trees, to the surrounding midlands district. By the 1890s the garden's collection of vines was the best in the area and included 1 000 vine cuttings from Constantia. The garden received little revenue from the fruit—"What with birds and boys"—but visitors could view the different varieties. Revenue from the sale of plants, on the other hand, was quite substantial: by the end of the nineteenth century it was put at £400 a year. The second Anglo-Boer War led to great destruction of fruit and forest trees in the Graaff-Reinet area with the result that in 1903 the demand for replacements was so high that local nurseries and the garden were sold out before the end of the planting season. That year the garden's sales reached a record £870: 33% of this was for fruit trees, 20% for forest trees, 12% for seeds and the remaining 35% for small plants, rose-trees, flowers and fruit. To cope with anticipated future demands, a piece of ground was taken near the Free Protestant Church to increase tree production and a new conservatory costing £200 was put up. A new illustrated catalogue (printed in Scotland) was issued and, as well as listing the plants for sale, it included gardening notes applicable to the Cape midlands district.

Admission of the public to the garden was not indiscriminate: visitors were checked in by a gate-keeper between 8 a.m. and 6 p.m. in winter and 6 a.m. and 9 p.m. in summer. Two notice-boards, one at each end of the garden, warned off trespassers. There were, however, few complaints of the public's behaviour either before or after 1900. The worst that happened was that blacks "hung over the walls of the fountain and the square reservoir", or visitors moved the seats, which also suffered from boys' carving their initials on them with their penknives. On one occasion a 506-metre (550-yard) length of barbed wire along the Bird Street boundary was maliciously cut. Visitors also cut holes in the nets to get at the fruit and the conservatory had to be kept locked against them.

The number of subscribers who paid the guinea membership fee varied from year to year but was never great, usually under 50. In the early years, plants to the value of half of total subscriptions to the garden were donated to the cemetery attached to St. James Parish Church and to the Jewish cemetery. Relations between the garden and the Jewish community were not always happy, however, the latter complaining that the garden was encroaching on their property; eventually the garden erected a strong barbed wire fence between the Jewish cemetery and the river and planted a line of stone pines along it.

Promenades and fêtes were regularly held in the garden. At a special garden party on 13 February 1903, Joseph Chamberlain and his wife were entertained. The previous week two local men, Messrs Neser and Ready, had given their irrigation water allowance to the garden to assist preparations. The effect was such that the Chamberlains expressed surprise at finding so fine a garden in the Karoo.

Like many other Cape botanic gardens, the Graaff-Reinet Botanic Garden was converted to sports grounds in the early twentieth century when it became the Urquhart Park, Rugby and Cricket Grounds. For the duration of its existence the botanic garden had received no monetary support from the Municipality and had to rely on the Government grant and on the proceeds of its sales of plants.

Rev. Dugmore's proposed layout for Queenstown's garden in the 1860s. The plan, in the shape of a crown, was not adopted. (Queenstown Museum)

Queenstown

The idea of establishing a botanic garden in Queenstown was first suggested during the 1860s. Rev. H. H. Dugmore produced a map of a possible layout for such a garden in the shape of a crown as an emblem of loyalty, with a statue of Queen Victoria as the central point and dwarf silver trees around the perimeter to represent pearls. This ambitious scheme was not carried out and it was not until 10 years later, in 1877, that a botanic garden was established on a 3,6 ha. (nine-acre) site on the north side of the town, on a truncated triangle bounded by Shepstone Street, Queen's Drive and Robinson Road. The property was vested in the Mayor and Council as trustees for the affairs of the garden and provision was made for the election of Committee members. A Government grant of £100 a year was obtained in 1879 and in 1883 the Town Council gave the Committee a loan of £1 000 at 6% interest to be paid off over a period of 20 years.

The first of five Curators the Queenstown Botanic Garden was to have in its four decades of existence as an independent institution was a Mr Day. He was appointed towards the end of 1878 at a salary of £150 a year plus commission on plant sales. He was also to have £35 a year for looking after the cemeteries attached to the Episcopal, Independent and Presbyterian churches. By the end of the century, commission had reached £170 on sales of over £1 200.

The grounds were cut in two in 1881 when the

Town Council built Alexander Road through them. The expense of four gates, two on each side of Alexander Road, was shared by the Town Council and the Garden's Committee. For some time the state of Alexander Road was a cause of friction between the Committee and the Town Council, the Committee complaining that the road was not completed and looked "like a neglected portion of the Gardens and forms a great eyesore". They offered to plant both sides of the road with trees if the Town Council would close it for a while. This the Council refused to do, but a compromise was reached in 1885 when the road was partially closed while the planting was in progress.

Partly to bring in income and partly to provide amenities for the townspeople, tennis courts and croquet grounds were laid out on the north side of the garden and later, when the garden became Town Council property, these were remade and new ones were added. The Committee, however, turned down a proposal to set up a skittle alley. The garden was further embellished in these early years by an obelisk erected by the 2nd Yeomanry Regiment in 1882–3 to commemorate the men killed in the ninth frontier war.

As elsewhere adequate water-supply was of prime importance. To start with, water was stored in a small dam and, with further supplies drawn from the town mains, the garden could rely on a few hundred gallons a week. But there were difficulties, for the garden was situated in the highest part of Queenstown where there was little water and where private houses were subject to water rationing. At the same time the construction of the railway line and its embankment in the early 1880s caused drainage difficulties. For example, a downpour of 18 cm. (seven inches) of rain in January 1884 caused £100 worth of damage and wiped out six months' work on the side of the garden next to the railway line and its embankment.

The increase of Queenstown's population in the late 1890s put a further strain on the water-supply. The Committee requested the Town Council to continue the submain water-pipe along Grey Street to the garden's boundary in Shepstone Street. This request was agreed to, the Committee paying £35 towards the costs. In the first year of the twentieth century the Town Council also bridged the water furrow in Queen's Drive to give easier access to the garden. In 1903 a 3,8 cm. (1,5 inch) borehole was sunk in the garden which found water at 75 metres (250 feet) and gave between 9 100 and 13 700 litres (2 000 and 3 000 gallons) a day. This, together with a Samson windmill, 120 metres (400 feet) of piping and a storage tank cost the Committee £210. To help meet the cost, the Town Council gave the garden a loan of £150 at a low interest rate. The Samson windmill was never very satisfactory, partly because a 2,4 metre (eight-foot) wheel was used instead of a 3 metre (10-foot) one. Eventually the water-supply problem was solved by the opening of the Bongola reservoir in 1907, and the windmill was sold.

The aims of the garden were clearly laid down at the time of its formation. It was to be "a nursery for raising trees and plants . . . a nursery and experimental Gardens . . . for the north east". It was to be laid out in flower-beds, lawns, shrubberies and walks. However, despite the emphasis on trade and pleasure, a conscious effort was made to lift the garden above the level of a commercial nursery and a park. As many plants as possible were labelled, first with zinc labels and later with porcelain ones. Varieties of aloe, opuntia and other succulents were made a speciality.

Membership of the garden was 10 shillings and sixpence a year and anyone paying one guinea or more could receive plants or seeds to the value of the subscription. A few years later rules of conduct were considered necessary, partly because of unseemly behaviour on Sundays and partly because of the theft of plants. Henceforth no dogs were to be brought into the garden, and trespassers found after closing time and people caught injuring plants were to be liable to prosecution. Due to the unruly behaviour of unaccompanied children in the past, no child was admitted unless accompanied by an adult. Babies in prams and even children in the care of a nurse were not admitted.

The garden was expected to pay its way and consequently it could not develop as a true botanic garden. Indeed, the Curator's report for 1893 acknowledged that it:

"had no pretensions to being a botanic gardens but that [it] is important as an experimental and nursery garden . . . the curator's chief aim [is] to be able to supply tree seedlings to meet public demand."

Originally the nursery which was to supply the demand for young plants—mostly trees and roses—was at the north side of the garden. The extent of propagation ground was very much enlarged in 1892 when the Town Council lent the committee 4 ha. (10 acres) on the north side of the railway line for a nursery. As this was some distance from the garden, a cottage for one of the white staff was put up in the hope that constant supervision would reduce theft to a minimum. This land was held on the option of the Town Council and so, to safeguard against summary eviction, in 1905 the Gardern's Committee took 8 ha. (20 acres) on a 14-year lease as a nursery on the far side of Queenstown, south of the Komani River.

Catalogues of the stock-in-hand were issued at intervals. In the early 1880s the garden offered 10 varieties of apple, 12 of pear, four of peach, eight of plum, three of apricot, three of nectarine and two of fig, all at three shillings and sixpence a tree. Vines were available in nine varieties and cost one shilling and sixpence for one-year-old stock and two shillings for two-year-old stock. Forty-six varieties of roses sold at two shillings and sixpence a plant. Blue gums were six pence to one shilling each and blackwood nine pence to one shilling each, as were *Pinus pinaster, P. pinea* and *P. strobus*. There were also offered for sale six species of cypress, three of thuya and three of acacia, as well as unspecified kinds of oak and liquid amber. The amount of stock varied from year to year but by the last decade of the nineteenth century the garden had 45 000 saplings in tins—mostly gums, especially rostrata and blue gums. As well as the trees listed from the early catalogue, there were now *Pinus vasigin*, Aleppo pine, Canary Island pine, *Casuarina lepto-clada, Acacia decurrens* and Catalpa ash. The stock of roses varied from 3 000 to 4 000 plants.

In the days before it became a public park the garden was thus a major source of supply of trees of all kinds for the surrounding district. To the garden also belongs the credit for having introduced fodder plants to the area. In 1892 the Committee made available plants of *Lathyrons wagneri* and of the Australian saltbush; in 1899 thornless opuntia was acquired from Cape Town Botanic Garden and free cuttings were distributed to farmers.

The garden's first Curator, Day, who had formerly been an assistant gardener at Grahamstown Botanic Garden, held the post for five years and was then replaced by a James Mason. Mason stayed for only two years but his successor, George Beck, who was appointed on 1 September 1885, remained as Curator for 14 years until ill-health forced his retirement in 1899. W. B. French, Assistant Curator to Beck for just under five years, then became Curator for a year

The band stand in Queenstown Botanic Garden.
(Queenstown Museum)

but he left the garden after an attack of typhoid fever in 1900 to go as a forester to the Indwe Railway, Collieries and Land Company.

His place was taken by M. Holly, from the Cape Town Botanic Garden, who was appointed as head gardener, but he in turn left in April 1902 and was replaced by a German, A. P. Paetzold, who was appointed Curator. Paetzold was largely responsible for building up the nursery stock of the Queenstown Botanic Garden. He seems to have been financially relatively comfortably off: he returned to Germany for three months in 1900 to get married, and in the same year lent the Garden's Committee £300, to be refunded in five years, towards the cost of building a cottage for himself in the nursery. Paetzold left the garden in 1904 after 11 years' service to work in the large nursery being developed in Bowker's Park. On his departure Holly returned to his old post and in 1909 was given the title of Curator when the garden became municipal property.

Apart from the Curators, the garden had other assistant gardeners from time to time. While Beck was Curator he usually had two skilled assistants and A. P. Paetzold's brother, Ernest Paetzold, was brought out from Germany in 1901 as an assistant gardener. Unlike many of the other Cape gardens, Queenstown used very little convict labour. In Beck's day there were 10 black labourers. The Garden's Committee paid tribute to one of its labourers in 1900 when it recorded . . .

"the great loss to the gardens by the death of Peter Jissong, a Cape boy and head of the native labourers who had done faithful work for many years."

Although Queenstown Botanic Garden was obliged to concentrate on the production of trees and shrubs for sale, nevertheless the Committee did provide green-houses for exotics. The first house, a structure 12 metres by 3,3 metres (40 × 11 feet) on the west side of the garden, cost £20. When it was destroyed by a hail-storm in 1882, it was at once replaced by a similar one with a large potting shed at the rear. A narrow seed-house, 30 metres by 2,4 metres (100 × 8 feet), was made for ferns in 1895 and two years later the old green-house was rebuilt and a new one of the same size constructed for just over £260. The Committee, now anxious for a stove-house for their garden, incorporated the material from the 20-year-old house to make one 12 metres long and three metres (40 × 10 feet) wide. No records have survived of the plants that the stove-house contained.

Queenstown Botanic Garden did not acquire a bandstand until 1900 when £200 was raised by public subscription for one to be used by the Queenstown Volunteer Rifles. This structure was erected in the north-east corner of the garden on a site 30 metres long and 21 metres (100 × 70 feet) wide, enclosed by a low fence. Here concerts were given on moonlit nights.

As has been pointed out, the garden was expected to pay its way by the sale of plants and seeds. Initially the income from this source was about £250 but by the time of the second Anglo-Boer War it amounted to £1 200. Hire of the tennis courts and croquet grounds brought in about £20 a year and the Government grant stood at £300. The expenses incurred in maintaining the garden at this time were £110 for seeds, £460 for wages to labourers, £390 for salaries for the white staff and £200 commission on plant sales to the Curator.

The immediate effect of the second Anglo-Boer War was to destroy the trade the garden had built up north of the Orange River. Sales dropped to a quarter of what they had been, although when the war ended they returned to their former value. However, in 1906, the Government grant was halved and the following year it was reduced to under £100. A further drop in sales after the initial recovery came in 1907 when the Transvaal banned the entry of any Eastern Cape produce because of the suspected presence there of *Plasmopara viticola*.

Nevertheless a minor triumph had come to the gardens in 1900. A photograph of a fine *Dahlia imperialis* grown in the Queenstown Botanic Garden was reproduced in the *Gardeners' Chronicle*. Subsequently, requests for seed came from Victoria Botanic Garden, Bombay, and from the Department of Agriculture in Washington, America. As the dahlia had not seeded, tubers were despatched to applicants.

Concurrently with its financial difficulties, the Committee began to change the nature of the garden. A number of large trees were cut and replaced by a rockery. Other trees were removed to make room for flower-beds and, for the first time in the history of the garden, grass plots were laid out. On 1 January 1910 the Committee placed the garden in the care of the Town Council and it was renamed Queenstown Public Gardens.

6 The public gardens and parks of the Cape

After 1877 no more botanic gardens were made at the Cape, but a number of public parks were established. By the 1870s Fort Beaufort, Humansdorp, Port Elizabeth and Uitenhage had such parks, and in the 1880s and 1890s a further nine settlements made use of a Government grant to lay out their own parks.

The inland parks

Alice in the Eastern Cape had a public garden which was established in 1892. As its annual Government grant was a meagre £25 it was much less splendid than the park in the neighbouring settlement of Fort Beaufort which received double the amount from the Cape Government. Alice Park contained two

Basic data on the public gardens and parks of the Cape

Place	Established	Date of first Govt grant	Size of Govt grant (in £)	Annual expenses (£)
Uitenhage	*c.* 1850	1883	*c.* 75	*c.* 200
Fort Beaufort	1860	1870	50	50
Port Elizabeth	1870	1870	450	2 020
Kimberley	1872	1881	300	690
Humansdorp	1876	1876	50	80
Aliwal North	1884	1884	50	220
Paarl	1885	1887	100	120
East London	1888	1888	150	350
Riversdale	1888	1888	75	90
Alice	1892	1892	25	50
Cradock	1892	1892	100	330
Malmesbury	1894	1894	?100	110
Mossel Bay	*c.* 1880s	1894	100	110

With the exception of Port Elizabeth, none of these parks was as expensive to run as a botanic garden. Since they were public parks most of them were not expected to be self-supporting and, in addition to the Government grant, they were given grants by the local urban councils. Alice Park's deficit was made up by the allocation to it of fines collected by the town under the Post Office Act; Paarl met its small debts by subscriptions and the occasional sale of flowers; Malmesbury was able to count on a third of the gate monies during the football season; Cradock was fortunate in that its Government grant was doubled in 1897 and it also benefited from the town pound's revenue. With the exception of Alice, East London, Humansdorp and Paarl, the Cape public parks sold trees to the surrounding district.

Irrespective of size the Cape parks had certain common features. They had gravelled paths which led through lawns and avenues of trees; they were usually fenced and the more fortunate parks had imposing entrance gates, donated by civic-minded patrons. Many had a cottage for the gardener, or in the more affluent parks for the Curator. Being for the most part controlled by the Town Council, they tended to have less difficulty in getting enough water than had the independent botanic gardens. Only some parks managed to acquire the much prized assets of a fountain, a glass-house, a bandstand, a pond for wild fowl and an enclosure for deer.

tennis courts and a croquet ground. It also had a number of public seats. The trees in the park were the subject of bitter complaint from the local council since the Forestry Department regulations prevented their being pruned or trimmed.

Of more account was the park at **Aliwal North.** When this was first established in 1884 it was called a botanic garden, but in 1895 it was redesignated a public garden. Like Humansdorp and Fort Beaufort parks, it was given a Government grant of only £50 a year. This did not dampen the enthusiasm of the inhabitants of Aliwal North who raised £2 000 to pay for the laying out and planting of the park. The result of this endeavour was that by the 1890s an avenue of trees led to the Aliwal North Park and a 9,2-metre-wide (10-yard) path winding through its 6 ha. (15 acres) gave "a cool walk in the summer time". There was a summer-house, a green-house, a maze, a pool, five bridges and a bandstand from which well-attended concerts were given on moonlit nights. The flower-beds displayed a good show of dahlias and chrysanthemums, and the grass was kept under control by the use of a lawn-mowing machine. It was claimed that the park was a very popular resort for invalids visiting the spas.

The park also served as a nursery for trees to plant on commonage and streets and to be supplied to the surrounding countryside. The importance of this aspect of the park was well expressed by Philip Brown, the Curator in 1893, "In these high altitudes one can travel for miles and not see a single tree

Aliwal North's garden about 1909.
(East London Museum)

which will give shelter to man or beast". Brown was at the park by 1889 and left in 1896, to be replaced by A. W. Higgins.

One difficulty the nursery experienced in raising young trees was that while water from the hot spa could be used for general watering the large quantity of mineral salts in it made it unsuitable for tree seedlings and they had to be watered from a well.

At the end of the century, the park was adversely affected by a combination of drought and a broken water-pump. To add to the park's difficulties, orders for plants were cancelled due to the second Anglo-Boer War. The occupation of the town by Orange Free State forces also prevented "the budding of roses and fruit trees" by the staff, now reduced to two. When the war was over the park was re-named the Aliwal North Public Garden and Nurseries.

Cradock's public park, established in 1892, was also to suffer from drought and war. Already in the 1890s, the drought had affected trees and plants in the town. The trees lining the streets, which had come from the park, were kept alive by people watering them by hand. In the park itself a water-cart was used with the satisfactory result that the area "maintained a bright and fresh appearance". This state of affairs lasted only until the outbreak of hostilities in 1899. The military authorities in control of the town water-supply then permitted the park only the overflow from the town furrow. The result was that for long periods the park

was without any water from this source and had to survive on water carried in buckets from the river.

With the war over, Cradock Town Council invested in a pumping machine which raised 114 000 litres (25 000 gallons) of water a day from the river bed. This benefited the park considerably and it very soon flourished. Its collection of trees, roses, chrysanthemums and dahlias was locally considered to be the best in the country. Interestingly, apart from Cape Town Botanic Garden, Cradock appears to have been the only garden or park to instal any sort of sanitary arrangement for the visitors. In 1902 two latrines, one for each sex, were constructed at a cost of £19.

The public garden at **Fort Beaufort** dates from 1860 when the town planted a group of trees in the form of a Union Jack to commemorate a visit from Prince Alfred. This plantation was referred to as Prince Alfred's Grove. The Town Council provided the area with an iron fountain, specially imported from England, 50 rustic benches in shady spots, two summer-houses, a high rockery surmounted by a gazebo, tennis courts and croquet grounds. The whole garden was surrounded by a hedge of roses, quince and Kei apple. It was not until 1879 that the Town Council succeeded in getting a Government grant for this park. Once this grant was obtained they soon replaced the hedge with a fence of sneezewood posts and barbed wire which cost £37.

In 1881 the Council was granted adjacent Government land which doubled the size of Prince Alfred Grove. In 1887 the Government gave the Council 55 ha. (135 acres) to establish Jubilee Park. The latter was requisitioned by the military as a camp for horses during the Anglo-Boer War.

In 1872, thanks mainly to the efforts of John Blades Currey, a park of 10 ha. (25 acres), known as the Kimberley Public Garden was set up in **Kimberley** by the Griqualand West Government. The Lieutenant Governor, Sir Owen Lanyon, gave his "fostering aid" and secured a small grant for the park. Lanyon was personally interested in botany and was in correspondence with Kew, as well as sending them seeds, including those of the baobab tree. The Kimberley Public Garden was also helped by the Recorder and Acting Commissioner, Sir J. D. Barry, who provided the park with convict labour. When the park was placed under the aegis of the Cape Colony in 1881 the annual grant was increased to £150. J. Rose Innes, at that time Acting Administrator, was well disposed towards the park and promised continued convict labour in the future. Further progress was made during the decade. 1884 was a particularly good year for the park: thanks to the availability of convict labour, in the early months some 20 men were working at any one time. That year saw the extensive planting of trees in the park, the plants being obtained from the Cape plantation at Tokai and from the Cape Town Botanic Garden.

The park was fortunate in being donated seeds and seedlings from private individuals as well as timber, which was used to construct seats. The London and South African Company gave the park's trustees a 50-year lease in 1887, the Civil Commissioner and the Mayor of Kimberley being custodians. In most years the rent was remitted.

A Curator or head gardener, called Glover, was appointed to the Kimberley park in 1883. After 1890 the post was filled by a man called Brown from England. He was replaced in 1900 by S. Woodhouse who had been head gardener to C. Ayres, a Cape Town florist. Two years later Woodhouse was succeeded by H. J. Holden, an Englishman who had been resident at the Cape for many years.

As was the case in Graaff-Reinet, the supply of water was crucial for the park's well-being. Initially the Griqualand Government sank a well in the grounds, but the amount of water from this source proved inadequate. By 1883 water was being bought from the waterworks company at a cost of £100. This provided water to the park for two-thirds of the year. In all, the park was by then using a million litres a year. To reduce this expense a swimming pool and a reservoir were built. These measures reduced water expenditure by a quarter. At the beginning of the twentieth century the construction of an additional reservoir costing £380 increased the water storage capacity to nearly two and a quarter million litres. Even this proved inadequate and to save water the swimming pool was converted to a manure store.

Not all the park was given over to pleasure grounds: part was used for nurseries, including a tree nursery and a rose nursery containing some 3 000 rose grafts. There was also a vineyard and an orchard. The amenity areas had flower-beds and avenues and groves of various species of trees. There was only one lawn, which was seeded with grass-seed obtained from Sutton and Co. in England, who also supplied flower seeds. The flower-beds and the avenues were edged with limestone and the gravelled paths were said to be the best in Kimberley. Indeed the whole park was the only open space of any attraction in the town.

Part of the grounds was sublet to various sporting bodies: the Ecclectric [sic] Cricket Club, the Kimberley Rifles, the Pirates Football Club, a tennis club and a bowling club. Between them they paid over £100 a year in rent. The park was fortunate in receiving not only a Government grant, which by the early 1890s had been increased to £300 per annum, but also annual grants from the Town Council and the Divisional Council totalling £200. The park also received £150 from De Beers and the London and South African Exploration Company.

Great inconvenience was caused to the park by the extension of the railway line in 1886. The park lost a large slice of ground used as the vineyard, and the reservoir at the north-east corner was partially destroyed. Fencing was broken down and trees felled. As a result of all this disruption, cattle intruded into the park and people took short cuts through it. It was several months before the fencing could be replaced and trespassers and cattle kept out.

The park became the site of the 1892 International and South African Exhibition. The Public Park's Committee appointed a sub-committee consisting of Messrs. Hogall, Nimes (the De Beers representative) and Wright to form an "improvement" committee to oversee the general enhancement of the park for this event. Their main task was to spend £500 laying out the grounds in front of the exhibition pavilion, fill up the old dam and make ornamental walks. Most of the trees transplanted for the occasion did not survive for long. Neither did a hedge of *Arborvitae* plants from the King William's Town Botanic Garden. These replaced the aloe fence round some of the flower-beds. When the exhibition was over Kei apple was used as flower-bed fencing. The prohibitive cost of the water needed to maintain the lawn in front of the pavilion meant that it could not be kept up. The large fountain in the centre of the lawn was retained though, as were the ornamental gates which had hung at each end of the main walk leading past the pavilion.

During the siege of Kimberley the British army commandeered the park. Much damage was done to

An interesting example of a gazebo or belvedere in Fort Beaufort's garden.
(Fort Beaufort Museum)

the gates, fences and trees before the park was returned to civilian control at the end of July 1900. No complaints were made concerning the behaviour of visitors until the war. Then, when the garden was open day and night, much damage was done and there was theft from the flower-beds even though the garden was patrolled by police.

Rent from the sporting clubs was lost and for a period there was a nearly total cessation of business in the nursery department. This soon revived and brought in a steady income of around £500 per annum. The years immediately following peace brought with them a welcome rise in the demand for plants, and sales rose to £960 in 1902 and to £1 300 in 1903. The Park's Committee failed in its claim for loss of rents but did succeed in getting £62 for wanton damage, though this was only two-thirds of the amount claimed.

Although no figures of attendance are available it is clear that the Kimberley Public Garden was much frequented. The concerts by moonlight and the promenades were greatly appreciated by the public even though the facilities available were limited. At first there were few seats for visitors, but in 1897 Cecil Rhodes and De Beers gave £75 to buy more.

As with Aliwal North, Cradock and Kimberley, the public park in **Malmesbury** was to suffer from the Anglo-Boer War. Its plantation of young trees was sequestered by the British army as a cattle compound. The trees were consequently greatly damaged and died. Moreover, the paths in the park were cut up and the entrance gates and perimeter fence destroyed. The military relinquished control of the grounds only after martial law was repealed in 1902. The park also had to cope with the problems of recurrent flooding as it was located on the banks of the river.

What became known as the Victoria Jubilee Park at **Paarl** began with an expression of civic pride. In 1885 a public meeting was called in the town to explore the possibility of establishing a park and £100 was collected for this purpose. The Municipality promised another £100 and, with Government consent, granted a piece of land for the project. The ground was fenced, a small conservatory erected and the Municipality provided free water. Many of the trees, shrubs and plants were presented to the park by local residents. Subscribers paid 10 shillings to 15 shillings a year which entitled them to enter and be accompanied in the park by a friend or by their family. By the early 1890s Paarl earnestly desired four amenities: the gravelling of the paths; seats; a fountain; and a bandstand. 1893 saw the provision of seats and by 1900 the other three wishes had been fulfilled. In 1894, B. P. du Plessis, J. R. Retief and P. W. Wessels, all of Paarl, jointly donated a fountain to the park which cost £100. At the same time a new conservatory was erected. The bandstand was situated in the centre of the park and cost £100, £20 of which was raised by public subscription. The source of funds to pay for many of these improvements, as for much of the running expenses of the park at Paarl, remains obscure.

The only other inland park in the Cape to receive a Government grant was the public park at **Riversdale**. Called Victoria Grove, this park was on the west side of the town on land donated in the late 1880s by the Municipality for the purpose of "tree planting and recreation". Victoria Grove was adjacent to the girls' public school and some distance from the older established Meurant's Park. The main problem concerning the well-being of Victoria Grove was a lack of available water. The park contained only two 1 800-litre (400-gallon) tanks to service the gardens. Meurant's Park was somewhat more fortunate as it possessed a dam with a 8 200-litre (1 800-gallon) capacity which was fed by the town's reservoir.

In 1894 when J. Frost, a member of the Legislative Assembly and Secretary for Agriculture, visited the town an appeal was made to him for more water. Frost's response was to suggest that the town save for a wind-powered pump.

The following year the Town Council financed the repair of the fountain and pagoda in Meurant's Park. In 1896 there was enough money to instal an Empire wind-pump with an 2,4 metre (eight-foot) diameter wheel in Victoria Grove. In a dramatic flood in 1902 Victoria Grove was all but destroyed. The park-keeper's house, fencing, gates and most of the plants were swept away. Only the rose trees and wind-pump survived.

QUEENS PARK, EAST LONDON.

Geometrical paths in East London's Queen's Park.
(East London Museum)

Parks of the coastal region

The first move towards a park in **East London** was made on 9 May 1878 when Mr Vincent, a member of the Board of Commissioners, made a recommendation that a site should be sought for a public park and botanic garden. At the end of the month Mr Murray, the Government Surveyor, was approached, and the title deeds for the agreed site were handed over to the Town Council on 17 December 1880. Additions were made to the site in 1882 and in 1892 which brought the area up to about 41 ha (100 acres).

For the first 15 years of its existence the park was managed by the Town Council, then by a Committee of Town Council members and "gentlemen selected by the subscribers". Advice on how to lay out and develop the park was given by J.C. Nelson, a local horticulturalist who owned the Cambridge Nurseries, and the work was carried out by six labourers under the direction of a foreman.

Initially priority was given to the construction of roads. By the end of the nineteenth century there were 2 000 metres (2 200 yards) of permanent carriage ways and 4 800 metres (5 200 yards) of pathways, and 3 700 metres (4 000 yards) of hedging had been planted, 2 800 metres (3 000 yards) of alternantheia and the rest of privet and tecoma. This work enabled the Committee to boast that there was no other park in the Colony with such amenities. It was the good carriage roads and the fine views from

the park that decided the Committee to drop the idea of developing it as a botanic garden and to consider it as a park only.

The formal opening of the park on 4 February 1890 by the Cape Governor, Sir Henry Loch, when the trees were hung with Chinese lanterns and a gondola floated on the pond, was made the occasion of a little showmanship between Loch and the Mayor. Loch asked the Mayor what name should be given to the park and the Mayor invited Loch to choose one. Loch made a show of considering the matter and then said that he thought it should be the Queen's Park. The Mayor replied that that would be a very suitable name.

The Municipal Council agreed in 1892 to make it a charge on the rate payers. The original Government grant was £50 a year and this was raised to £150 in the early 1890s. The cost of running the park varied between £600 and £700 a year, of which about two-thirds went on wages.

During the first five years of the park's existence several developments took place. A site for a bandstand was cleared and prepared by the men of the Kaffrarian Rifles under the direction of Major Carroll and his officers. The major also made a donation towards the cost of erecting the bandstand, and when it was completed the band of the corps gave concerts there.

The entrances to the Queen's Park were greatly

enhanced by the donation of three sets of wrought iron gates. John Stroyan gave a pair for the main entrance on Pontoon Road and Sir Donald Currie M.P. and James Georgeson J.P., the Chairman of the East London Harbour Board, each gave sets—probably those now at the Park Avenue entrance. It gave the Committee much satisfaction that the Stroyan gates were in full view of passengers disembarking from ships at the landing stage.

The Town Council gave extra water to enable the vlei to be retained and this made possible the introduction of wild fowl, which included black swans, Carolina ducks, crowned cranes and mandarin teal.

A massive fountain costing £100 was donated by M. M. Fleischer, Civil Commissioner and Resident Magistrate. This 1,2-metre-wide (four-foot) fountain was installed on a rise in the centre of the park by the firm of Nicobay and Pape. At the same time mains water was connected to the lake and fountain.

By the mid-1890s the Committee had come to the conclusion that a Curator, or at least a head gardener, was essential for the park. In 1895 C. Franz was appointed as Curator. Franz occupied the position for only a year and then was moved to the curatorship of the town's recreation grounds. His replacement, W. H. Wormald, had acted as Secretary to the park's Committee since at least 1888. He in his turn was replaced by the former Curator, C. Franz, in June 1903.

The number of black labourers, paid between two shillings and two shillings and six pence a day, fluctuated between six and a dozen, but it was a problem to get them to remain in employment, or indeed to get them to do fulltime work. Another problem for the Curator was the theft by the public of flowers, fruit and birds' eggs, and dogs also caused a certain amount of damage.

In the last year of the century, electric light was installed, and by that time there was a greenhouse 12 metres long by nine metres (40 × 30 feet) wide as well as an office for the Curator. The status of the Queen's Park was raised in 1895 when the Government selected it to undertake trial crops of bananas and pineapples. These trials were carried out until well after the end of the second Anglo-Boer war. The fruit from these experimental crops, when not stolen by the public, was sent to the Frere Hospital.

The area of the park was substantially reduced by the construction of the railway line in the early 1900s. None the less a tree nursery was introduced and an extra 2 ha. (five acres) of veld was reclaimed and made into ornamental grounds with 125 varieties of roses. There was a temporary reduction in the number of visitors, however, due to an overflow of polluted and smelly water from a culvert serving a new residential area. Still later in the century the park, which now contained a small zoo, was further reduced in area by the construction of a new road. The remaining area has been designated a National Monument.

The lake in East London's Queen's Park.
(East London Museum)

The Park, Humansdorp.

Published by Hallis & Cº, Port Elizabeth.

The jungle-like interior of Humansdorp's park about 1907. (East London Museum)

The park at **Humansdorp** had its origins in 6,5 ha. (16 acres) acquired about 1865 to establish a forest plantation to encourage tree planting in the area. In 1876 Smyth, the Civil Commissioner, spurred on the Divisional Council to apply to the Government for a grant for a park. The vestry of the Dutch Reformed Church gave 2,8 ha. (seven acres) in perpetuity at the southern end of the settlement for a site. By 1878 a capital outlay of £102 had provided the park, drawn to a plan by W. A. Muskett, with a substantial sod wall to keep out cattle, and with handsome iron gates. Walks in the form of the crosses on the Union Jack were laid out. Four carriage drives eight metres (25 feet) wide and four footpaths five metres (16 feet) wide met at an ornamental fountain on the site of a drained vlei in the centre of the design. These were well gravelled. Nearly 5 000 trees and shrubs were planted; of these 500 were purchased from the botanic garden in Grahamstown, which also donated some plants. The rest of the trees were raised in the park and, thanks to the orders of the Civil Commissioner, planted out by convict labour.

The park continued to be extended and improved during the 1890s. It was fortunate in having an unlimited supply of water. Tennis courts and croquet lawns were laid out; and cultivation was generally improved. The "town's ladies" were made responsible for the rose and other flower-beds and under their supervision great progress was made. To celebrate Queen Victoria's Jubilee in 1897 the Dutch Reformed Church donated a further 3,6 ha. (nine acres) which were used as a nursery. There does not appear to have been any selling of plants or of cut flowers although small quantities of firewood were sold.

The park was successfully run on the annual Government grant of £50 and a Divisional Council grant of about the same amount. At the end of the nineteenth century the Government grant was doubled. In 1901 the Humansdorp Park was transferred from the care of the Divisional Council to that to the Municipal Council, whose first acts were to replace the old sod wall by a paling fence and appoint J. Roth as Curator.

A park at **Mossel Bay** was already in existence at the end of the 1880s. In 1894 it was given an annual grant of £100 and the following year the park was considerably enlarged by a grant of Government land. The Municipality was far from pleased at the quality of this extra ground. It was, they said, poor, dry, sandy ground and the entrance was through a piece of land which was "all holes and refuse tips". Furthermore, the park was now subject to flooding from two deep ravines on this land. The construction of a wide, paved, deep drain, leading from the head of the park on the Cape Town road down to the sea, cost the town £150 but largely solved the problem.

The Park's Committee was, however, grateful to the Government for its annual grant which enabled it to hire two labourers at a cost of £1 a week. Convict labour was used for watering in the park and the cost charged to the "streets account". By 1899 the Council could point out that despite the extra money expended on the bad land, the park did have

A view in St George's Park in 1878, contained in the *Gardeners' Chronicle*. This Port Elizabeth garden had the rare distinction for South Africa of having an illustration in this famous horticultural magazine.

rustic seats, a fishpond (fed with water from the town's supply) and a large number of shady trees, including seven Norfolk Island pines. There was extensive planting of *Pinus halepensis* on the drifts of white sand that lined the Cape Town road. Further embellishments included the erection of a fountain in the pond, which was closed off by iron railings and surrounded by grass lawns. The park remained open until 7 p.m. By 1902 it had become greatly appreciated by the townspeople.

Port Elizabeth was in the unique position in the second half of the nineteenth century of having adequate money to finance three parks, St. George's Park, founded in 1861, Prince Albert Park, opened in 1863, and Victoria Park, established by the early 1890s.

The first move to obtain ground for a public park in Port Elizabeth was made in June 1861 when H. W. Pearson, M.L.A. applied for a grant of land "for a public playground". His application was seconded by Mr Slater and a committee consisting of Messrs Pearson, Slater, Reed, Impey and Kirkwood was appointed. An area of about 73 ha. (180 acres) on the hill was secured and named St. George's Park. The opening was celebrated "with champagne and innumerable toasts drunk".

Through the good offices of R. W. Murray, the Secretary of the Cape of Good Hope Agricultural Society, and one-time editor of the *Cape Argus* and founder of the *Eastern Gazette*, John Wilson, head

gardener to Rev. John Fry at Rondebosch, was persuaded to come and establish the park.

John Wilson, who had been born in Scotland in 1830, moved to Port Elizabeth where he lived at Richmond until 1874, when he moved into a house built for him in the park. At first he was just head gardener, but by 1877 he was being called Superintendent and at his death he was known as the Conservator of Parks and was earning £225 a year.

He came to develop a flat area of dry, bare, rocky ground and many considered that he would not be able to make much of it. But he worked hard alongside his labourers, often from dawn to dusk, and by 1863 he had developed an inner oval area about 740 metres long and 460 metres wide (800 × 500 yards), bounded by a road or carriage way. Inside this oval area he made a cemetery of under half a hectare (one acre), a cricket ground of about 1,6 ha. (four acres) and an arboretum of 2,5 ha. (just over five acres). The rest of the allocated area was set aside for development to bring an income to the park.

Wilson was an upright, reserved and unassuming man. He was pleased when he obtained some goldfish at a very reasonable rate for the park and he refused, when asked, to cut the first sod of the bowling green in the park—a ceremony then carried out by Cecil Rhodes. It is said that when Wilson's wife asked him why he did not bring her some flowers from the park he replied, "I cannot. They

The Pearson Conservatory in Port Elizabeth's St George's Park was opened by J. X. Merriman in 1882.
(Port Elizabeth Museum)

are not mine". Wilson died on 25 March 1889, leaving 10 children. An elder of the Presbyterian Church, he was buried in the presence of members of the Scottish Association in the cemetery he had created. He was succeeded as Conservator of Parks by John T. Butters.

In 1880 the Director of Kew made reference in a speech of the "remarkable groups of succulent plants in the garden at Port Elizabeth". It was not, however, for indigenous flora that the park was to become famous. As early as 1883 it was admitted that there was little ground for planting because St. George's Park provided facilities for the athletic club, four football clubs, and a quoits club as well as having three cricket grounds and the first bowling green constructed in South Africa. In the mid-1880s this bowling green was extended to cater for the large increase in the number of players. Today the park is internationally famous as a venue for test matches. In Prince Alfred Park, too, three cricket clubs occupied the greater part of the ground between the main gate and the keeper's cottage, thus precluding any further planting of trees.

St. George's Park also contained amenities other than the sporting ones. There were two ponds, one with wild fowl on it, spurwing geese, "mountain geese" (shelduck), wild duck, cormorants and swans. This pond was surrounded by 1,5 metre (five-foot) palings to protect the birds from "dogs and idle youths", and later the fence was "improved

with barbed wire". The park had an enclosure for deer as well. In it there were six fallow deer presented by Sir Henry Loch, Japanese deer sent from the Royal Zoological Society in London, bushbuck and springbok. The other pond was an ornamental one in the middle of the park. It had a fountain in the centre, and by 1881 was enclosed with iron railings.

The main entrance to the park was embellished in the mid-1880s when ornamental iron gates, flanked by Norfolk Island pines, replaced the previous wooden gates. The old gates were removed to the south side of the grounds for the convenience of the Port Elizabeth cricket club.

In the early years there were two small conservatories in St. George's Park, one for ferns and one for orchids. At the end of the 1870s the Committee decided that a large house was desirable. It will be recalled that in 1875 the firm of J. Boyd and Son of Paisley put up a cruciform conservatory with a central dome in the Cape Town Botanic Garden and that the Government gave £1 000 towards the total cost of £1 600. In 1879 John Wilson was sent to Cape Town to inspect the conservatory and to confer with the Cape Town Superintendent, McGibbon. What Wilson saw and heard satisfied him and it was decided that Port Elizabeth would also have a Boyd glass-house.

Boyd supplied one of their standard houses, shipping it out in sections, and a member of the firm,

Mr Frazer, came to supervise its erection. Frazer worked in association with two local architects, first with a Mr Wicksteed, then after Wicksteed's death with H. W. Miles, the town architect. When finished the glass-house was very much a British production. Chance and Brothers supplied the glass, Birt and Nephew, ironmasters at Colebrookdale, sent out eight iron seats, the vases for plants came from J. Rosher and Company of London and the fountain from Boyd. At the same time two gardeners attached to the nursery firm of Henderson and Sons were brought out from England, one to be in charge of the conservatory and the other to be in charge of the plant nursery.

The opening ceremony was performed by J. X. Merriman on 13 September 1882. The building was named the Pearson Conservatory in honour of the founder of the park. The conservatory, of wrought iron, moulded teak and glass, consisted of an oval central dome 8,7 metres (29 feet) high with a short axis of 7,5 metres (25 feet) and a long axis measuring 15 metres (50 feet), and two wings each 5 metres (17 feet) high, 13 metres long and 6,3 metres wide (44 × 21 feet). The dome was supported by eight marbled pillars and iron ribs strengthened by ornamental iron scroll work. Inside, the basic colour was a warm grey, with pale blue and light chocolate, and the iron work was a light flesh tone. The ornamental heads of the eight pillars supporting the dome were picked out in gold and dark green. The outside was light stone with chocolate and white linings and the ornamental iron crestings of the roof and terminals were a dark blue picked out with white and gold.

To guard against sun-scorch the dome was of light blue frosted glass, as were the sides most exposed to the sun. Window sashes were painted white and each alternate sash was hung on a pivot. The roof sashes were opened by a lever operated by a hand screw.

The main feature in the dome was a fountain standing in a basin surrounded by four bronze seats. The whole inside perimeter was flanked by a raised bed for plants within a holding wall and in the centre of both wings a double tier of perforated iron shelving was supported by miniature iron columns.

The cost of the Port Elizabeth conservatory was about twice that of the one in the Cape Town Botanic Garden. Iron, glass and wood came to £1 560, freight from England and duty to £336, and digging the foundations and erecting the house to £1 904, giving a total cost of £3 800. Parliament promised to give £1 000 towards the cost but in the event gave only £750. The Town Council donated £1 050. To meet the deficit the outstanding money was borrowed from the town improvement fund and repaid at £250 a year plus interest over a period of eight years.

The conservatories erected by Boyd at Cape Town and Port Elizabeth were more sightly in appearance and more soundly constructed than the one the firm supplied to Dublin Botanic Gardens. This house, completed in 1860, was so ill-proportioned, with a 18-metre-high (60-foot) dome towering over small side wings, that it was roundly attacked in articles in the *Gardeners' Chronicle*. The construction of this conservatory was so faulty that five years after it was finished stays had to be inserted because of the oscillations during stormy weather and in 1883 Boyd had to dismantle the dome and rebuild it. Both Cape Town and Port Elizabeth were more fortunate as their Boyd conservatories required only normal repairs and repaintings.

At the beginning of the 1970s the Port Elizabeth municipality contemplated taking down the Pearson Conservatory. Wiser counsel prevailed and by 1982 this important glass-house was restored. It is now a National Monument. A similar situation arose about the same time in Belfast, Northern Ireland, when the City Council proposed to demolish the curvilinear glass-house in the city's botanic garden and replace it with "a nice modern structure". The wings of the Belfast glass-house are one of the earliest authenticated examples of the work of Richard Turner, the great ironmaster who built, and probably helped to design, the Great Palm House at Kew. As in the case of Port Elizabeth, conservationists succeeded in saving the Belfast house and it was restored and reopened in 1983.

No figures were kept which would give an indication of how many people enjoyed the park's amenities. The only pointer as to numbers is that the extension of the railway to Port Elizabeth in 1878 brought in many visitors from outlying areas and there was a vast increase in the number of visitors and picnic parties 10 years later when the tramway was extended to the park.

The initial government grant of £250 a year had risen by the end of the century to £450. The grant from the municipality varied from year to year according to the cost of running the parks; it had risen to £1 000 a year by the mid-1880s.

Initially the sale of cut flowers and garden plants and tree saplings from St George's Park brought in about £300 a year, but in 1884 the sale of flowers and plants was discontinued as the municipality wished to stop the park's trading role. The sale of young trees was not affected by this decision as such sales, of between 2 000 and 5 000 saplings a year, were for the most part to the municipality for street planting. Christmas trees and cut boughs continued to be supplied for festivals and bazaars, cut flowers were sent every week to the town library and the hospital, and potted plants went to the horticultural society and to the City Hall.

The cessation of the trade in potted plants and cut flowers reduced the value of sales to around £50 a year, but as the Municipality subsidized the parks the loss of revenue did not have the catastrophic effect it would have had on a botanic garden unsubsidized by the Municipality. Financial security also resulted in no experimental work being carried out into crops of possible economic value. The lack of scientific research was glibly explained away with the statement: "Plants of economic or commercial value have no place in here due to the hard, rocky nature of the site".

Apart from the salaried staff, the wage bill for labourers was just under £1 600 at the outbreak of the second Anglo-Boer war, though it is not clear how many staff were employed. During the war refugees were employed in the city's parks.

Expenditure on the three parks varied from under £2 000 a year to over £3 000 of which wages, salaries and maintenance accounted for about two-thirds of the total. Very little, usually under £50 a year, was spent on seeds and plants. However, plants were exchanged with other Cape gardens and with overseas gardens, including Kew. A Wardian case came from Australia in 1878, for instance, filled with half-a-dozen tree ferns, all over two metres (six feet) high.

In 1846 the Government granted the town of **Uitenhage** a piece of land lying between Market Street, Chase Street, the Town Hall and the Caledon River for use as a market place. When the area proved to be bigger than was needed for that purpose the portion next to the cemetery for blacks was laid out as a park. Cape Town Botanic Garden sent a Wardian case filled with plants in 1862. As the town expanded the ground was needed for building purposes, so in 1877 the park was moved out to College Hill, further from the town centre. About 1,6 ha. (four acres) of what was to be the new park had already been planted in the early 1870s with blue gums which, it was hoped, would relieve a threatened shortage of firewood.

Part of the College Hill site had been granted originally to a Prussian immigrant, John G. Schlemmer. Schlemmer was born in June 1789, came to the Cape in 1811 and died at Uitenhage in February 1875. He was instrumental in developing the town's water supply—even by 1895 only two streets had a sure supply—and in 1834 he erected a windmill and a watermill on his plot in Cannon Street beside College Hill. Today four of the millstones from the mill can be seen in the park.

By 1882 the College Hill Park had been renamed the Magennis Park after James Magennis, who served as Mayor of Uitenhage after it was made a Municipality in 1877, and who died in August 1897.

Later in the century two other parks were created. The Victoria Park owes its origin to the introduction in the early 1880s of the American custom of school children planting trees on Arbor Day. Until late in the century Victoria Park was essentially a plantation of trees. James Magennis saw to it that there was a sufficient supply of water for the pines, oaks, blue gums, hakeas and acacias planted there. Boys, cows and horses caused a great deal of damage and by the end of the century Victoria Park was virtually a recreation ground. The remaining trees were used for defence work during the second Anglo-Boer

War. Ultimately it became the site of the Uitenhage playing fields.

The third Uitenhage park, the Jubilee Park, was laid out on the north-west side of the town, facing the Dutch Reformed Church, in June 1887. Its development took some time, for the Department of Forestry regulations required that all ground designated for planting be trenched, a slow operation at best, and, as the Curator said, "doubly so with convict labour". It also suffered from insufficient water; a grove of orange trees failed and so did other trees.

The three parks, Magennis, Victoria and Jubilee, were cared for by one Curator. The first Curator was an English gardener, Richard Horne, whose rather splended title was Corporation Nurseryman and Park Superintendent. When he was appointed is not known, but he held the post until he died in August 1882. "An earnest worker in the cause of temperance", he was buried in the Congregational cemetery. Robert Cruickshanks, Horne's successor, held the post for a short time and then H. Fairey, a Scot, took over and remained, first as Curator and then as Superintendent, until his death early in the twentieth century. Until the mid-1930's George Cartwright had charge of the parks; he died, aged 70, on 21 December 1939.

Although Fairey held one of the lesser posts in the Cape horticultural world he was not afraid to voice his criticism of the conditions under which the gardens and parks in the Colony had to operate. He resented having to sell seedlings and bunches of flowers. He claimed that because the garden had to attend to the business of selling to the public there was little time for making experiments into the economic and medical value of plants. Fairey also complained of an inadequate water supply, the lack of a seed room and an office, and the fact that unlike "all British gardens and parks there was no enclosure for staff and labourers to do their work". The necessity of having to use a scythe which he believed was "now almost an obsolete implement" in European gardens further annoyed Fairey. Generally he felt that Magennis Park had not lived up to the expectations of its founders.

Fairey was one of the few Cape Curators to complain constantly of the public's behaviour. The wanton damage, theft and rowdy conduct of youths on Saturday afternoons greatly disturbed him, as did the damage done by cows and horses to the 2 200 trees planted in the streets of Uitenhage. In 1896 the land between Riebeeck College and the Magennis Park was acquired. Subsequently this area had to be wired off to prevent access by the boys of Muir Academy who pestered the staff and girls of Riebeeck College.

Fairey went home to Scotland for five months in 1898 and during his absence the parks were run by J. King from St. George's Park in Port Elizabeth.

The Magennis Park was the most important of Uitenhage's parks. Covering 6,5 ha (16 acres) by the end of the nineteenth century, the Magennis Park contained an oval lawn, flower beds, plantations of trees and an area of uncleared bush. From the entrance in Cannon Street the main walk led through the park. A bypath called Lovers' Walk passed the Curator's house and led to the bush. All paths were surfaced with local sand. The flower beds were filled with roses, dahlias, English lavender, pyrethrum and mountain pansy *(Viola lutea)* of which Fairey was particularly proud. A maze of Kei apple was made in 1895 to a plan supplied by J. T. Butters of Port Elizabeth, but it was not a success and five years later it was grubbed up and replaced by a croquet ground. The most outstanding feature of the Magennis Park was an avenue of deodar cedars. There was also a line of Monterey pine *(Pinus radiata)*, hundreds of grevilleas, cypresses and various other pines. A source of special pride was a collection of English apple trees.

As far as garden buildings and garden ornaments went, Magennis Park was moderately well equipped. There was an obelisk commemorating the Basuto war. A bridge over the main water furrow near the mill house connected the north-east entrance with a side walk. A bandstand surrounded by gum trees stood in the centre of the oval lawn and there the band of the Uitenhage Volunteer Rifles frequently gave concerts. A reed-thatched plant house contained a good fern collection and a span-roofed glass-house put up at the end of the 1880s had hot water pipes put in at the end of the second Anglo-Boer War. While the Cannon Street entrance left much to be desired, the Graaff-Reinet Road entrance was adorned by iron gates hung on pillars erected during the last year of the century. In the mid-1890s a horticultural hall was put up on rising ground overlooking the flower garden to act as a home for the Uitenhage Horticultural Society, which organized shows, fêtes and promenades. However, just before Union, the hall was let and turned into a skating rink.

The amount of money spent on the Uitenhage parks was not great and never approached what was available to the Port Elizabeth parks. It was not until 1883, when the town had had a park for over two decades, that a Government grant was applied for. At first the grant was only £50 a year, but by the end of the 1890s it had been increased to £200 annually. As in the case of the Port Elizabeth parks, the annual grant from the Municipality varied more or less according to need. Sales of cut flowers and plants rarely amounted to more than £50 a year and were often much less.

It was the opinion of Fairey, who, like MacOwan at the Cape Town Botanic Garden, loathed having to act as a shopkeeper, that the relatively small sale of plants was due to the presence in the area of nurseries run by competent men. One of these nursery firms, Smith Brothers, was sufficiently well established to publish annually its *Guide for the garden*. This was more than a mere catalogue of plants for sale: it was a comprehensive gardening book on the cultivation of flowers, vegetables, shrubs and fruit trees. The 1894 edition, which was probably the first, ran to 288 pages, with 16 pages of advertisements of the firm's products. It was printed by H. M. Pollett of London and sold at 10 shillings and sixpence a copy. Other editions followed.

On the whole, income varied from under £200 a year in the early days to around £600 a year at the end of the nineteenth century. The Curator was lucky if he got £100 a year income from his salary and commission on sales, but he did have a free house. Wages for the labourers—the number varied from year to year and was usually about a dozen —fluctuated around a total of £200 a year.

SECTION B: 'THE GARDEN COLONY': NATAL

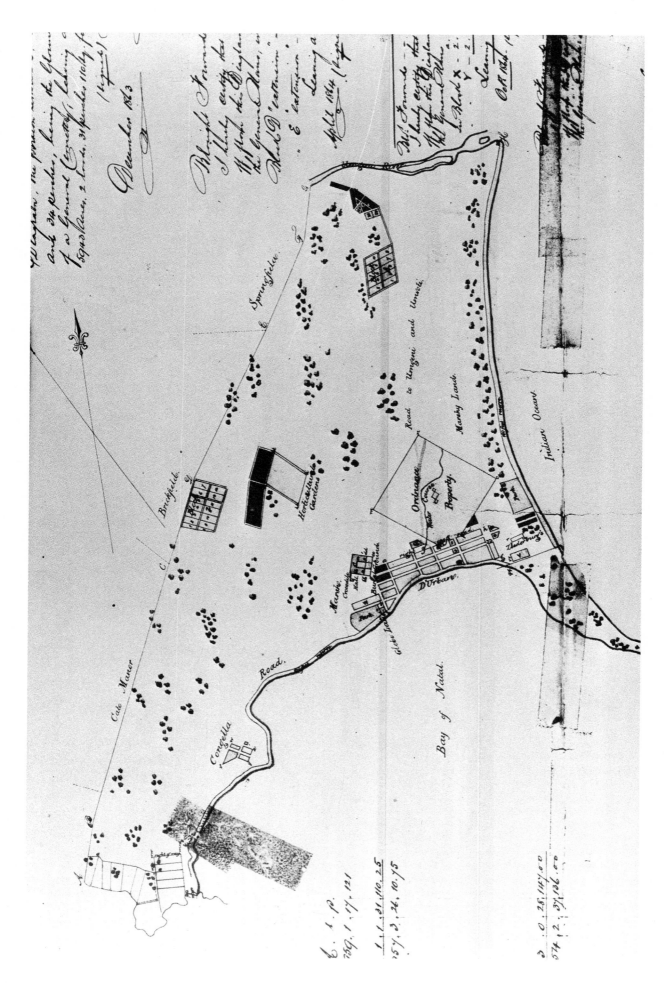

Map of Durban in the early 1850s showing the settlement and the garden.
(Durban Local History Museum)

7 Durban: The early struggle, 1848–1881

The proliferation of botanical institutions in the Cape in the nineteenth century was not matched by Natal, where only Durban on the coast and Pietermaritzburg 80 kilometres (50 miles) inland established botanic gardens. The impoverished nature of the Natal economy right up to the Union in 1910 and the general indifference of most colonists were factors which threatened even the existence of these two gardens. None the less, the gardens in Durban and Pietermaritzburg were to have a considerable impact on the development of the young colony. The Durban Botanic Garden in particular was, by the 1890s, to achieve a world-wide reputation as being one of the foremost botanical institutions within the British empire.

Durban's international reputation was due primarily to the pioneering work of its Curator John Medley Wood. Prior to his appointment in 1882 the Durban Botanic Garden had had a rather chequered existence. It was established by the Natal Agricultural and Horticultural Society, a body which came into being in April 1848, the same year Natal achieved its own separate colonial administration. Indeed the Society's formation by such leading colonial figures as Sam Beningfield, 'Joe' Cato, J. F. Kahts, William Stanger and Edmund Morewood may be seen as part of the wider process of establishing the new Colony.

Three abortive attempts were made to acquire land for the society's "experimental" or "agricultural" garden. Sites at Umlazi, on the banks of the Umgeni river and near Congella proved either unsuitable or unavailable to Dr. Charles Johnston, the Society's Supervisor. In the interim before a permanent site was found, what plants the Society possessed were kept by Sam Beningfield. This was to prove quite a time for it was not until 11 June 1851 that it was finally agreed to establish the garden permanently on 10 ha. (25 acres) of ground on the lower slopes of the Berea overlooking the sea.

The plot was surrounded by crown land and was near to land used by John Cane, the early settler who became an Nguni chief. It was also adjacent to the famous Currie's Fountain. No road led to the garden which was some three kilometres (two miles) across the flats from the village of D'Urban; 12% was flat swampy vlei and for many years of little use. The rest of the ground was scrub bush, sloping steeply with a fairly loose poor red sandy soil. A further 10 ha. (25 acres) was soon added to the garden, the 20 ha. (50 acres) being officially granted by Lieutenant-Governor Pine to the Society on 8 September 1854. This desire to acquire a large acreage was the first of many mistakes made in establishing the garden for, with the very limited resources available to curators, the area was just too big to manage properly.

From the outset the role of the garden was decreed. It was to experiment with the cultivation and propagation of indigenous and foreign plants of an economic and commercial value to the Colony. In 1867 when the government grant was increased the Colonial administration actually insisted that the growing of plants "as objects of curiosity and interest" should be made an "incidental and secondary aim" of the garden. From 1850 until the late 1860s the Society held annual exhibitions or shows sometimes in Durban itself, but usually at the garden. At these events substantial prizes were given for ploughing and for the best varieties of crops exhibited. In 1859 three silver cups were made available for competition. Occasionally, as in 1851 and 1862, Natal produce for imperial exhibitions in London was displayed in the garden.

As the Society could offer the Curator only a salary of £50 a year plus accommodation, which proved to be a large hut for the first few years, he was allowed to supplement his income by selling surplus plants from the garden privately to the public. This arrangement was stopped in 1860 when the Curator's salary was raised to £150 per annum, a level at which it remained until it doubled 30 years later. However, the inadequacy of the Government grant (£50 in 1853; £100 in 1858; and finally £350 after 1865) encouraged the continuance of sales to the public for the Society's benefit. From being of £50 value or 13% of income received in 1866, by 1903 the sale of plants to the public was netting £3500, some 70% of revenues. In 1900, for example, the Durban Botanic Garden sold seven tons of green mangoes to a chutney factory.

Subscriptions might have prevented the increasing reliance on revenue from sales of plants but the number of members fell steadily over the years, from 81 in 1851 to 30 in 1910. Subscribers were permitted to recoup their subscription, usually one guinea, in flowers, plants, seeds and fruit from the garden. They could, in common with visitors from up-country, visit the garden any day of the week. The general Durban public was only allowed into the garden on Wednesdays, Saturdays, Sunday afternoons and public holidays. Not until 1882 did the garden open every day to the general public.

The subscription system did not work and revenue from subscriptions never exceeded 13% of total annual revenue. Sales remained the chief source of extra income. The consequence of this was that curators were diverted from the primary role of providing a proper scientific botanic garden into that of establishing what was in effect a commercial nursery.

Primarily responsible for this development was a fiery Scot named Mark Johnston McKen who was

Mark McKen (1823–72), curator of the Durban Botanic Garden,
1851–53, and 1860–72.
(Botanical Research Institute)

Curator between 1851 and 1853 and again from 1860 to 1872. He was described as "stockily built, except for a rather aggressive sandy moustache that sprouted beneath his sharp nose, like the hairs on an ear of oats".

He was said to be a heavy drinker who, on his death in April 1872, left his wife Margaret destitute with six young children to rear. The Horticultural Society raised and invested £600 for her benefit. But as a collector of plants, birds and butterflies McKen was superb. He, William T. Gerrard and McKen's great enemy John Sanderson, the president of the Horticultural Society and proprietor of the *Natal Colonist,* for many years supplied Kew with a steady flow of indigenous plants, mainly from within a 50 kilometre (30-mile) radius of Durban. In 1869 McKen published a pamphlet entitled *The Ferns of Natal* and the following year he and Gerrard brought out their *Synopsis filicum capensium.* In 1867 McKen, now often referred to in Natal as the "Professor", spent seven weeks in Mauritius returning with a large collection of plants for the Durban Botanic Garden. However, his enthusiasm for collecting led to the Horticultural Society's Committee reprimanding him in 1865 and instructing him to concentrate more energy on the Society's garden.

McKen was 27 when he arrived in Natal from Jamaica via England in October 1850. Though he did not take up the curatorship until June 1851, he had brought with him from Kew a large collection of food plants which he delivered to the Horticultural Society. While this benefited the young Colony, it did little to help the garden, which by 1856 had virtually become McKen's private farm: he employed the labour, sold the produce and provided plants only to those subscribers whom he chose to favour. Consequently the reputation of the Horticultural Society became badly tarnished. On 3 August 1861 the *Natal Star* commented:

> "It is no doubt a matter to be regretted that so little interest is taken by the Public in a society which might be of great utility to the colony. It was a subject of remark and regret at the last annual dinner that the Natal Agricultural and Horticultural Society did not represent the Agriculture and Horticulture of Natal, and if that remark was applicable at the time we have seen nothing in the subsequent proceedings of the society to redeem it from the imputation."

McKen, who contrary to popular belief was not trained at Kew, failed to establish a proper botanic garden. Under his direction no more than 10% of the garden's acreage was cultivated; the rest remaining fairly wild bush. Plants were not bedded according to families, but planted willy-nilly. No attempt was made to establish an arboretum, pinetum, herbarium or proper nursery. Worst of all, McKen failed to label the plants in the garden, with the result that when he died no one knew what was where. This was unfortunate as McKen did have a fairly solid knowledge of botany and he even took the trouble to learn the Zulu names of indigenous plants. But he was lackadaisical in displaying his collection. As late as 1867 Sanderson wrote to Kew indicating that it was a waste sending McKen a collection of West Indian orchids (Kew correspondence 1353).

In the intervening seven years between McKen's two stints as Curator (1853-60), when he was managing a sugar estate at Tongaat, the turnover of curators was so great (seven in all) that little was achieved. The only possible exception to this succession of undistinguished curators was Robert Plant, who was to be one of the first botanists to collect in Zululand. He was Curator between 1854 and 1856 and is generally regarded as the founder of the ill-fated Natal tea industry.

Matters were not helped by the fact that the 1850s were very wet, 295 cms (116 inches) of rain falling in the year 1855/56. The visiting Committee of the Horticultural Society constantly complained of the mud they encountered in the garden. In April 1859 a temporary Curator named De la Chaumette complained bitterly of the devastation caused in the garden by the rains, the porcupines and trespassing oxen and horsemen. Some fencing was erected in 1863 but by 1869 most of it had been stolen or broken down. The result was that not only oxen but occasionally lion, too, were to be found in the garden in this early period. With a large number of mosquitoes breeding in the vlei it is little wonder that few people visited the garden save when the town closed up and trekked over the flats to the undeveloped Berea for the annual agricultural show.

None the less by the late 1860s a combination of threats, an increased Government grant and tighter Society control coupled with Government inspection was playing dividends. McKen was forced to concentrate increasingly on the upkeep of the garden so that gradually it began to be more attractive. From the entrance at the bottom of the grounds a path wound its way up the hill round the garden. Two summer-houses were built from which an excellent view of the town, sea and bay was afforded. There was a hurricane shed, office, small house for the Curator, double brick-lined pit for propagating and a couple of small ponds. These ponds were the only source of water and in the dry season labourers had to carry buckets of water from them up the hill to water the upper garden. In 1869 a 14 000 litre (3 000 gallon) tank was constructed in this higher part, but in time of drought, as in the late 1870s, it and the ponds dried up and the garden suffered badly. The planting of a cactus hedge round part of the grounds in 1871 partially solved the problem of trespass, but the Sydenham Road boundary remained open until late in the century.

A balanced view of the garden from an anonymous lady appeared in the *Cape Monthly Magazine* in the mid-1860s. Part of her account ran as follows:

> "The Gardens cover fifty acres of ground, and, being so large, are ill-kept in one sense, though they are very creditable in another. The show of flowers is very poor. Indeed, the place resembles a large plantation or shrubbery more than a garden. There are scarcely any tropical plants or trees not represented here, and the scene strongly reminds one of the torrid zone. Only the palm is wanting in its full developed glory . . . the support of the towns-people has almost ceased . . . At present it [the gardens] is little more than a wilderness—though a very luxuriant and a very varied one."

Despite the fact that by the late 1860s McKen had built up a collection of some 300 indigenous species, including a giant cycad, it was not until 1871 when a small green-house, nine metres by 4,5 metres, (30 × 15 feet) was erected in the grounds by Thomas Drew, at a cost of £105, that more than a handful of visitors ever came near the garden. The opening of Botanic Gardens Road in 1873, connecting the garden with Berea Road, cut out the direct and unpleasant route across the flats and encouraged a rise in visitors. Rickshaws often plied between the town and the garden in the 1870s, but it was only when Botanic Gardens Road was hardened in 1883 that many carriages ventured out to the garden. By then McKen was long dead and the botanic garden was slowly beginning to recover from his legacy.

Between January 1873 and December 1881 the Durban Botanic Garden was in the capable, but tied, hands of William or Julius Wilhelm Keit. Born in Saxony in 1841, Keit received his training as a gardener at various botanical institutions in Dresden, Munich, Basle, and Brussels, before working as

William Keit (1841–1916), curator of the Durban Botanic Garden, 1873–81.
(Mrs K. Plekker)

a gardener at the Exhibition Palace in Dublin between 1866 and 1867. Though he thought Dublin a dirty city he enjoyed his time there. When the Exhibition Palace went bankrupt Keit had to forsake their "winter gardens" and for part of 1868 worked as gardener at Blyth Hall near Worksop in Nottinghamshire. In May of that year, however, he returned to Ireland to work in the Glasnevin Botanic Gardens on the outskirts of Dublin. Here he became head foreman in charge of the propagating houses, a position which well prepared him for the heat and humidity of subtropical Durban.

Keit was a serious and hard-working young man. Medley Wood later described him as "peculiar", and certainly Keit had little time for those in Natal whom he regarded as charlatans. He was fluent in German, French and English, though it was an early complaint in Durban that he could speak no Zulu. Keit freely admitted his deficiency as a taxonomist. Writing to Sir Joseph Hooker from Glasnevin in August 1872 he observed,

> "My botanical knowledge is more general than particular. I can arrange plants botanically after knowing their names, but I could not undertake to know or describe new plants scientifically." (K.C.776/777)

It was on the recommendation of Hooker that Keit, then aged 31, was appointed Curator of the Durban Botanic Garden. His fare out to the Colony was paid by the Horticultural Society. After a bad voyage out to South Africa, during which the ship's screw broke rounding the Cape, Keit arrived in Natal on 14 November 1872 in good time to take up his new appointment on 1 January 1873. In the nine months since McKen's death the garden had been allowed to deteriorate. Paths and borders had been washed away, the vines were covered with mildew and the palm house contained only a few ferns and fuchsia. Somewhat disheartened, Keit reported back to Kew that the garden was very much neglected:

> "There is no systematic arrangement, the plants having been planted where there was space and what I regret most, that there are no names on them. It will take me a long time and all my energy to bring something like order in this place and to rename the plants." (K.C.778)

His list of what plants did exist in the garden included varieties of balsams, zinnia, gomphrena, gaillardia and verbena.

Keit threw himself energetically into re-establishing his garden, and he was soon boasting to his friends in Dublin of the bougainvilleas, the roses and the variety of fruits he was nurturing. Kew tried to help him as much as possible; in September 1873 a large Wardian case arrived full of yam, tobacco and orchid plants. Despite numerous difficulties, Keit tried his best to establish a proper botanic garden and in the process put a final stop to the holding of fairs in the garden. New ground was cleared and an attempt was made to group together individual plants of the same order. A pinetum was established containing 27 different varieties of conifer. In the nursery he experimented with the growing of yams, opium poppies and a variety of types of tea, coffee and rubber. But he was most of all fascinated by the growing of palms. He also annually distributed, often free of charge, thousands of silver oaks and eucalypti *(Eucalyptus globulus)* to applicants in the Colony. In 1873 he planted 2 000 of the eucalypti in the swampy ground adjacent to Durban town. To improve the quality of the soil, in 1876 Keit came to an agreement with the town's Sanitary Department and a 5 cm (two-inch) layer of manure was spread throughout the lower garden.

With the opening of Botanic Gardens Road, Keit constructed a new entrance to the garden onto St. Thomas Road and built a small bridge at this gate over the ditch which ran down the side of the grounds. His efforts to provide effective labelling met with only limited success. He tried lead, cast iron, pine and zinc labels. Medley Wood later experimented with enamel and teak labels, but he, like his predecessor, was defeated by a combination of climate, vandals and white ants.

There were, however, much more serious problems facing Keit in his endeavours. He was constantly short of manual labourers. McKen had over a number of years built up a black labour force of six, to whom he paid 10 shillings to 12 shillings per month as well as providing them with food rations. He had a good rapport with these men, who, he said, "know their work well". On more than one occasion McKen allowed these workers to leave the garden to collect for him in their home districts. To supplement this small labour force McKen came to an agreement with the Resident Magistrate in 1866 whereby six short-term convicts from the Durban central jail worked at the botanic garden and the Horticultural Society paid the wages of the accompanying police constable.

Keit inherited this system, although for reasons of expense and because of the demand for convict labour in harbour construction, in 1877 only three convicts could be acquired for the garden. The black work-force was less reliable under Keit and very often he had only three workers to keep the garden in repair. For three years he had an indentured St. Helena boy working for him and he had several white assistants for short periods. But generally the labour situation was most unsatisfactory and Keit himself was often reduced to performing manual labour. Worse was to come with the outbreak of the Anglo-Zulu War in 1879 when the entire black labour force disappeared, never to return. Although more blacks were eventually employed Keit began to indenture Indian labour, a process continued by Wood until 1906. Initially three Indian workers were indentured and housed at the garden.

The problem of having no skilled assistance became more acute when a Government meteorological station was installed in the gardens and the Curator had to take twice daily readings. Thanks to Keit, an accurate record of Durban's weather exists from 1873, but the cost to the botanic garden was great. In spite of previous Horticultural Society promises, Keit was now unable to collect plant specimens in Natal and Zululand. By 1875 he was complaining bitterly to Kew that he was never able to leave the garden (K.C.793). This caused considerable annoyance to Sir Joseph Hooker who, like his father before him, had for long taken an interest in the exciting flora of Natal. Since the 1840s the Hookers had encouraged collectors from the Colony to supply the mother country and other botanical institutions with specimens of euphorbia, orchids, succulents, cycads, palms and ferns. These independent collectors included Thomas Baines, Rev. John Buchanan, Edward Button, John Dunn, Maurice S. Evans, William T. Gerrard, Katharine Saunders, John Sanderson, T. R. Sim, William Stanger and Dr. P. C. Sutherland.

That the Curator of the Durban Botanic Garden in the 1870s was prevented from fully participating in this exchange of plants was viewed in a dim light by the Director of Kew. In September 1873 Keit was reduced to sending Hooker the seed cone of the cycad in front of the Curator's house, apologizing that "our Garden yields nothing you might care to have". As McKen had "stripped" the surrounding countryside of interesting plants Keit found himself unable even to maintain the old system of exchanging plants for botanical periodicals. Dr. Moore occasionally sent his ex-foreman botanical literature all the same.

On top of this irritation Keit found himself Curator of a garden starved of money. Shortly before his arrival the Horticultural Society was reduced to selling many of the garden's tools. Throughout his eight years as Curator, the garden's real income never exceeded £420 per annum, of which 70% had to be spent on salaries, wages and rations. Subscriptions never exceeded £65 in any one year and were usually under £40. Never more than £120 per annum was spent on maintenance and building, with the consequence that by 1879 the green-house was in such bad repair that its roof collapsed.

To compound the crisis for the garden, drought hit Durban in the 1870s. By 1878 annual rainfall was down to 71 cm. (28 inches); it had been 140 cm (55 inches) in 1874. With the tanks and ponds dry many plants died, the nursery being especially affected. The digging of large holes to collect water gave only limited relief. During these dry years the white ants did considerable damage, especially to Keit's much prized collection of palms. When the rains finally returned in 1880 they washed much of the loose sandy soil down to the vlei. One of the few surviving accounts of the garden at the time paints a sorry picture. Mary Elizabeth Barber was motivated to visit the Durban Botanic Garden because butterflies fascinated her and the garden had a reputation for being a lepidoptera sanctuary. In 1879 she wrote of the garden:

> "They are too remote to be of any real advantage to the inhabitants. Public Gardens are public property . . . These gardens are "out of sight and out of mind"; no one appears to either think or care about them; they have a weedy and neglected appearance. The conservatory was empty. In its vicinity, some fowls that seemed to have the run of the gardens were scratching among the weeds and fallen leaves. Near the springs of water we observed some plants which had been potted for sale. There are, however, in these gardens, some remarkably fine exotic trees from tropical regions, especially of the Palm tribe, growing half wild amidst the forest, with no one to admire their beauties."

Mrs. Barber continues by saying she met the Curator (Keit) who gave her a large bunch of blue waterlily flowers *(Nymphoea stallata)*. When she begged him not to pick so many Keit merely replied that she was welcome to them as "no one ever came to look at them in that solitary place". When Mrs. Barber took the flowers to Durban many people expressed surprise that she had got them from the botanic garden. Such was the ignorance in Durban of its only proper garden.

As early as December 1873 Hooker had realized the impossible position Keit was in and offered him a possible appointment elsewhere (K.C.791). But by then the Curator was engaged to Anna Louise Currie, the daughter of Durban's future Mayor, Mr. H. W. Currie (Mayor 1879–80), and Keit was reluctant to leave the Colony. Thanking Sir Joseph for his offer Keit expressed his determination to create a true botanic garden, but he added. "Should I fail then I trust you will not forsake me." The couple married in September 1874 and although happy together, illness and death struck their young family in the late 1870s. "Doctor and Undertaker", wrote Keit, "have shared between them the small savings I had managed to scrape together" (K.C.819).

By 1881 Keit's position was fast becoming untenable. A considerable number of Durban's citizens openly blamed the dilapidated condition of the gardens on its Curator. Behind this was Keit's hostility to the idea that the grounds should be used as a pleasure park. The fact that Keit was a foreigner did not endear him to some members of the Horticultural Society. An inheritance enabled him to resign his position and he left the garden in December 1881. Though he had failed as Curator, Kew recognized the circumstances of his quitting and Thistelton Dyer resolutely defended Keit against attack.

It is interesting to note that William Keit proved himself an excellent Superintendent of Durban's public parks. He was the driving force behind the establishment of Congella and Bulwer Parks, and laid out Albert Park, Queen Victoria Park and the City Hall Gardens. The palms along Victoria Embankment are also a legacy of his endeavours. As well as these achievements he established a nursery and dairy on Berea Road which duly prospered. An avenue off this thoroughfare still bears his name. William Keit died in 1916 leaving eight children.

8 Wood and the Natal Botanic Garden, 1882–1913

By 1881 the Durban Botanic Garden was in a sorry state: buildings were dilapidated, borders and flower-beds in disrepair and large parts of the grounds overgrown. With Keit's departure the fate of the garden was in the balance. Sir Joseph Hooker lambasted the Natal Agricultural and Horticultural Society for its lack of enterprise and its negligence. It was obvious to those colonists interested in botany, such as Messrs Aiken, Evans, Jameson, Shepstone and Greenacre, that drastic action needed to be taken in order to save the botanic garden from becoming a mere public park. Fortunately the Colonial Administration recognized that, despite its many defects, the Durban garden had in the past rendered useful service to the developing Natal economy. Thus it was decided to undertake a radical re-organisation of the administration and control of the garden.

The first of several significant steps in this direction was the appointment of John Medley Wood as Curator, despite stiff opposition from a rival claimant, the self-opinionated J. L. Meade. Wood had excellent qualifications for the difficult task of re-establishing the botanic garden. He was of early settler stock, his father, James Riddall Wood, being a well-known local solicitor and amateur botanist. Wood himself had arrived in Natal at the age of 25 in 1852, having spent seven years as a junior officer on an East Indian merchantman. He took up farming, first at Otterspool at the mouth of the Umdloti River where he had only limited success in the growing of arrowroot, cotton, coffee, sugar and castor oil. Later, he moved inland to Inanda where he ranched, grew timber and ran two local trading stores. Interestingly, Wood's sister had married the garden's early Curator, McKen. Thus, as in many other Victorian botanical institutions, including Kew and Glasnevin, a dynasty was established. Wood was later to employ his stepnephew, Walter Haygarth, as a research assistant and artist.

When living at Inanda, Wood became seriously interested in botany. During long walks he collected plants which he later dried and preserved. He corresponded with Kew and in 1877 published a pamphlet entitled, *A popular description of the Natal ferns*. Two years later Wood and the amateur botanist, Rev. John Buchanan, wrote *The classification of ferns*. So enthusiastic did Wood become about his hobby that when he was offered the curatorship in 1882 he accepted it, ignoring the detrimental effect of the coastal climate on his health. He took up his new post on 1 March 1882. Wood served as Curator until 1903, when he was given the title director to facilitate the promotion of his head gardener. Wood remained as Director until 1913. For 33 years he watched over the fortunes of the Durban garden.

John Medley Wood (1827–1915) was colonial Natal's most famous botanist. He was curator and later director of the Durban Botanic Garden from 1882 to 1913.
(Botanical Research Institute)

The diminutive Medley Wood was a popular choice as Curator. At 56 he had considerable standing in the community. He was interested in football and cricket, he was an office-bearer in the Berea Presbyterian Church and he was already respected by the leading botanists and collectors in the Colony. This regard was not undeserved for Wood was an excellent taxonomist, pre-eminent in his field in Natal and surpassed in the subcontinent only by MacOwan and Bolus at the Cape. As well as being a Fellow of the Linnean Society, Wood was a corresponding member of the British Pharmaceutical Society. In 1913 the University College in Cape Town awarded him an honorary doctorate, the graduation ceremony being performed in the grounds of the Durban Botanic Garden.

A new curator was not the only change to affect the botanic garden. Equally important was the new dispensation under which the garden was to be administered. By Law Number 21 of the Colony a new Durban Botanic Society was incorporated on 12 November 1883. By deed of transfer dated 9 January 1884 the new Society took over control of the garden from the now defunct Horticultural Society. The function of the new Society was described as the "maintenance of the Botanic Gardens for the introduction, cultivation, propagation and distribution of plants of every climate". The new Society was empowered to borrow upwards of £1 500 on the security of its lands to raise capital for improvements to the botanic garden. Should the amount raised by subscriptions and donations not exceed £150 for the three succeeding years, the garden was to become the property of the Natal Government. A new administering committee of nine members was to be appointed, including two Government representatives and the Mayor of Durban, and henceforth the official title of the garden was to be the Natal Botanic Garden, a change which caused some anger in Pietermaritzburg, where a botanic garden had been in existence for nearly a decade. The duty of taking twice daily meteorological readings was transferred to the Natal Observatory, which acquired 0,8 ha. (two acres) of the Society's grounds.

Thus Wood was in a considerably more advantageous position than his predecessors. Not only was he free to indulge in collecting expeditions but, because of the prospect of raising loans, he was able to employ professionally trained gardeners. Over the next 30 years such men as Messrs Bartlett, Boutell, Farrell, McAlpine, Rutter and Thorn were employed in the garden at one time or another. The most important of Wood's assistants was James Wylie. He arrived in Durban from Kew a month after Wood's appointment in 1882. Though only 20 years old, Wylie made an excellent head gardener and right-hand man to Wood. His work in the nurseries dramatically increased the garden's revenue. By the mid-1890s this exceeded £2 000 per annum and in 1905 it reached a record £5 000. With such sums available Wood and Wylie were able to establish what the *Kew Bulletin* in 1910 described as a botanic garden which stood apart from any other in the continent.

This international reputation was largely achieved because of the activities of the newly established herbarium which was attached to the Natal Botanic Garden. Wood had accepted the curatorship under the condition that he be allowed to form a herbarium. He was already in possession of some 1 500 dried specimens which he had collected at Inanda as well as 200 preserved American plants which a Mrs Edwards had presented to him. To this small collection was added a large parcel of plants donated by Kew, and a hotchpotch of Australian and central African plants which had belonged to Rev. Buchanan and which was eventually donated to a botanical institution in Berlin. Finally, Wood discovered the remnants of what had been the Gerrard and McKen collection. The bulk of the originals had long since been sold in England. In 1882 most of what was left was unlabelled, had not been properly preserved and had fallen victim to a combination of ants, rats and damp. In total Wood's herbarium filled only two cabinets and was housed in

a small dilapidated wood and corrugated iron building.

This situation might well have continued had not the celebrated Dr P. C. Sutherland taken an interest in the embryonic herbarium. Remembered as the man who looked after the young Cecil Rhodes on his arrival in South Africa, Sutherland was Natal's Surveyor-General and a man of considerable influence in the Colony. In 1884 he persuaded the Executive Council in Pietermaritzburg to take over responsibility for the herbarium. This they did in 1885 when 0,8 ha. (two acres) were ceded to the Natal Government for what was henceforth to be called the Colonial Herbarium. Wood was appointed its Director, a position he held until his death in August 1915.

Thanks to Wood's energetic programme of collection and plant exchange with other botanical institutions in South Africa and abroad the Colonial Herbarium grew rapidly. In 1887 it numbered some 5 000 specimens of which 70% were South African plants. In a decade the total number of specimens had more than trebled and by 1904 it had reached 31 000. In 1913 the herbarium collection, then housed in 54 cabinets, stood at 45 000 specimens of which 13 000 were South African. From 1905 it became considerably more comprehensive and never contained more than 29% South African plants.

Although in practice the herbarium was an integral part of the botanic garden, because it was controlled by the Government rather than by the Durban Botanic Society, it received a separate grant independent of that given to the garden. This herbarium grant eventually rose to £300 per annum though it was never more than 12% of the total running cost of the whole botanical institution. Another advantage of Government control was that when it became obvious that a purpose-built herbarium was urgently needed to house the collection it was the colonial administration which shouldered the expense. Because of Wood's insistence on the construction of a foundation which could carry a possible future second storey the costs of this building exceeded £2 000. Designed by Wood's relative, Walter Haygarth, the new herbarium, which was occupied in 1902, was a majestic single-storey building with a fine double flight of steps leading up to the entrance. The collection was housed in a long room with a high ceiling and the library and workrooms were housed in the two wings. Wood's hopes of a technological museum in an enlarged building never materialized, though in 1903 he did start a small botanical museum.

Many of the South African specimens housed in the Colonial Herbarium were collected by Wood himself. Every year he set out in a wagon, very often ignoring the unsettled state of the Colony. For example, in December 1900, he was collecting in the

The Colonial Herbarium. This building was erected in 1902. By 1913 it contained 45 000 specimens of dried plants. Medley Wood hoped that one day a second storey would be added to accommodate a museum of economic botany.
(Durban Local History Museum)

vicinity of Ladysmith despite the proximity of an international war. The 1906 disturbances did, however, keep him at home. One major gap in his trips was the black reserves which Wood considered at times too dangerous to enter. In 1884 he stated that he would need a police escort to venture into one of these. None the less he did journey through large areas of Natal and Zululand, though he only twice ventured beyond the Colony's perimeters. John Dunn, Thomas Baines and other celebrities in the rural parts were always ready to provide Wood with hospitality and any exciting plants they came across. It is a measure of Wood's success as a collector that he is credited with the discovery of no fewer than 62 new species of plant.

In the herbarium Wood and his staff of three or four dried, poisoned, classified, named, labelled, mounted on white paper, indexed and placed in cabinets every new plant which arrived. Many of the specimens had to be sent to Kew for identification, and after 1903 Wood entered into lengthy correspondence with Harry Bolus at the Cape on plant identification and general botanic matters. Thanks to the generosity of the retiring Governor, Sir Henry Bulwer, the herbarium acquired a microscope in 1884. This proved a considerable boon especially as Wood, like Keit, had eyesight problems.

The South African collection of dried plants was relatively comprehensive though deficient in Cyperaceae and grasses. Wood made ample use of the collection and over a period of 30 years published a series of botanical monographs. These included *The Flora of Durban and Vicinity* (1887), *An Analytical Key to the Natural Orders and Genera of Natal Indigenous Plants* (1888), *A Preliminary Catalogue of Indigenous Natal Plants* (1894), *A Handbook to the Flora of Natal* (1907) and *Revised List of the Flora of Natal)* (1908). In addition to these works or books Wood wrote impressive catalogues of the plants contained in the botanic garden (1883, 1889, 1897 and 1915) as well as annual reports for the garden and for the herbarium.

Both McKen and Keit had attempted—not very successfully—to build up a small library at the botanic garden, the first book acquired being *The Gardener's Encyclopaedia of Plants* which was bought in 1854 for 30 shillings. Keit collected the *Gardeners' Chronicle*, but it was not until Wood's period that the library grew. Even then it was not comprehensive. In 1886 Wood listed its contents, by then housed with the herbarium. As the property of the Botanic Society he noted the following: *Flora Capensis* (three volumes), *Harvey's Genera, Synopsis Filicum, Flora of Tropical Africa* (volumes 1, 2 and 3), *Hong Kongensis, Paxton's Botanical Dictionary, Industries Bermays, Flora of British India* (volumes 9 to 12) and the *Gardeners' Chronicle* (volumes 1 to 3 and the current numbers). As well as these the herbarium library contained Wood's own books. These included *Flora Mauritianus, Treasury of Botany* (1866 edition), *Select Plants, Bentham's British Flora, Class Book Botany, Natural History* (King), *Mono Ebenacreae* (Hiern), *Synopsis Colonicacea* (Baker) and *Synopsis Alameae.*

As the years passed Wood spent an increasing amount of time in the herbarium. He carried out research into plant dyes, plant poisons and drugs, and plant diseases. He investigated European and African food crops and for a period concentrated on experimenting with the fibres *Sesbania bispinosa, Crotaiaria juncea,* flax and hemp. The value of plants for medical research was also investigated by Wood. He recommended *Monsonia biflora* as a cure for dysentry, and investigated *Mikania guaco* as an antidote for snakebites. The conclusions to his many researches he published in numerous articles, letters and reports. Many of these were of tedious length and incomprehensible to local farmers and horticulturalists. None the less, Wood was influential in the horticultural development of the Colony and he never hesitated to answer enquiries even when these seemed ridiculous, as with the farmer in 1895 who demanded that Wood produce a grass which would remain green throughout the dry season.

Wood was not slow to voice his views on subjects which he felt concerned the well-being of the Colony. He was particularly disturbed at the destruction of the bush vegetation and pressed strongly for a ban on blacks removing firewood and grazing cattle around springs and near river banks. Wood's appeal to be allowed to teach botany in Durban schools was rejected by the Council of Education in 1882 though he did occasionally give lessons in a few private schools. Equal lack of success attended his attempt to persuade the Durban corporation to line Durban's streets with trees. "Though often taken into consideration this has as yet been scarcely commenced". In fact, the first proposal of this kind dated back to 1855.

Nor did Wood hesitate to complain about the amount of work which fell on his shoulders. On one occasion in 1892 he was reprimanded by Kew for grumbling about not having the strength to bother identifying properly specimens he had sent to London He wrote, "At my age, 65, one scarcely feels fit for closely examining plants after a day's hard scrambling through bush" (K.C.1843).

Kew was not displeased, however, with the major enterprise undertaken by the Colonial Herbarium, the publication of a series entitled *Natal Plants.* In 1894 Maurice S. Evans suggested to Wood that they jointly write a volume on plants used by Africans for medicinal purposes. Wood declined because he believed the medicinal value of African drugs "are but little understood by the Natives, and whatever value certain of them may have the Native system of administering them is wholly mixed up with charlatanry and superstition". It was decided therefore to undertake a book on Natal's flora and Evans stood guarantor for the publishing costs. Fortunately the

Government considered this project of value to the Colony and agreed to subsidize a series of volumes at the rate of £130 per volume, or £32/10/- for each of the four sections of a volume.

The publication of *Natal Plants* extended over the period June 1898 to April 1912. Evans and Wood co-authored the first volume, after which Wood took full control of the project. In all, six volumes were published. Part of a seventh was written but never completed. Because of the additional Government grant, Wood was able to expand his herbarium staff: as well as an Indian technician, named Mr Moonsamy, he employed Walter Haygarth and Frieda Lauth. Both drew plates for *Natal Plants* and worked hard on the preparation of the volumes. Allegations were made that Wood did not give enough credit to these assistants and after Miss Lauth married and left the herbarium comments were voiced in the local press to this effect. Wood's retort was, "Neither Mr Haygarth nor Miss Lauth wrote a single description for the work 'Natal Plants' and Miss Lauth did not have 'practically sole charge of the work' for a single day". Frieda Lauth, now Mrs Floyd, had great ability and went on to become a distinguished botanist in her own right. Her place in the herbarium was filled by Miss M. Franks who had been employed since 1901. Miss Franks was responsible for many of the plates in the later volumes of *Natal Plants* and served 13 years on the herbarium staff, in turn being succeeded in 1914 by Miss K. A. Lansdell, an artist of some talent.

Natal Plants contained much new material on the flora of Natal. Only volume two on the Colony's grasses proved a disappointment. Much of this was merely a reprint from *Flora Capensis.* There was some general criticism of Wood's texts. The *Journal of Botany* in 1900 (vol. 38, pp. 192–3) commented on this:

"... when a man is working in an herbarium, we must be satisfied with bare descriptions of the parts, but we expect more from the man in the field. Notes on the colour of the culms, sheaths, leaves, or spikelets, and on the general habit and habitat and the nature of the ground, give life to the description; and in the case of a colonial publication like the present add considerably to the value. Such notes are, however, very rare."

Generally, though, the response to *Natal Plants* from the botanical world was favourable. The *Kew Bulletin* spoke of "taxonomic work of a high scientific value" and in 1905 the herbarium was honoured by a visit from Professor Engler, the President of the British Association.

Although Wood had built up an institution of international repute this did not impress many of the colonists, who considered the herbarium a waste of public money. On his own admission, Wood conceded that none of the public ever came near the herbarium and in all his years as Director he alone had made use of the collection. In the late 1890s a correspondent in a Durban paper alleged that he had been refused entry to the herbarium and its library. The correspondent continued:

"On telling my experience at your garden to an old Durbanite he said, 'You must not take our Botanic Garden seriously. Of course we must have Botanic Gardens, as a child must have the measles; and although with us the complaint is chronic, it is in such a mild form we don't know we've got it'."

Attacks like this undermined the local reputation of the garden to such an extent that when Natal plunged into yet another financial crises after 1906 the Government, as well as halving its grant to the botanic garden, abolished its grant to the herbarium. This resulted in Wood's having to lay off staff and reduce wages. Between 1907 and 1909 the survival of the herbarium seemed in considerable doubt. Following a visit of the Minister of Agriculture a greatly reduced grant allowed a temporary stay of execution. It was only because of the intercession of J. Burtt Davy, the Government Botanist to the new Union administration, that the grant to the herbarium was raised to £260 per annum, thus allowing volume six of *Natal Plants* to be printed.

When the Union Government took the policy decision to downgrade the Natal Botanic Garden in 1913 they also decided that the herbarium be allowed to continue as before in Government hands, but completely separate from the garden and controlled from Pretoria. Even spare copies of *Natal Plants* were bought up by the Government for £300. The 0,8 ha. (two acres) containing the herbarium and the Curator's house were fenced off. Wood relinquished his directorship of the garden, but retained that of the herbarium. He was also permitted to remain in the Curator's old house, where he died on 26 August 1915 at the age of 87. For the herbarium it was the end of an era and though its activities were to be greatly expanded, especially after 1919, no future Director was to have such an impact on its development as did its founder, a man whom Professor J. W. Bews described as the "father of Natal botany".

When Wood succeeded to the curatorship in 1882, as well as establishing a herbarium he set about constructing a proper infrastructure for the garden. This entailed initiating and finding finance for a substantial building programme in addition to securing a more satisfactory supply of water for the garden. The latter problem was solved surprisingly easily. Following negotiations the Durban Corporation agreed to construct a reservoir in the grounds of the botanic garden. This was not for the sole use of the garden but was aimed at servicing the growing town. None the less it did provide the garden with a more dependable supply of water. The reservoir, with a capacity of 228 000 litres (50 000 gallons), was completed in June 1884.

Wood's building programme was not so easily carried through. In November 1882 the Botanic Society asked the Natal Government for a loan of £750 to enable it to undertake several major construction projects. The most Wood had been able to achieve till then was the building of a small fernery, costing £13. To his astonishment the Government refused the loan and suggested the garden apply to the Supreme Court for relief. This proposal came to nothing. It was only when the Botanic Gardens Law was enacted in 1884 that the Botanic Society was able to look elsewhere for finance. Immediately they issued seven debentures of £100 each giving an interest of 7% per annum. This money was spent over the next year on a number of schemes. A new office for the garden and an adjoining cottage for the head gardener were built on the St. Thomas Road boundary, the two buildings costing £328. At a cost of £287 a small conservatory was also constructed to replace the one which had collapsed a short while before. This palm house survived until 1901 when it was converted into a store for nursery plants. As well as these major building projects a number of small tasks were undertaken, including path and water tank construction, and new tools and flowerpots were purchased.

Throughout Wood's period much capital was spent on building and maintenance. Between 1875 and 1903 the sum allocated annually to this rose by some 25% and by the turn of the century building costs often consumed over 30% of the annual expenditure. After the 1884 venture three further major building projects were undertaken. As mentioned previously, in 1902 a fine herbarium building was erected, but before that in 1889 construction commenced on a new house for the Curator. The Curator's previous house, said to be the oldest house on the Berea, was small and badly in need of repair. Most of the capital to build a new home for Wood was raised at a bazaar in July 1889. A year later the new house was completed. It was large, attractive and spacious, and very much a suitable official residence for the Curator of what was by then one of the most beautiful botanic gardens in Africa.

Seven years later in October 1897 work was completed on a large green-house, named the Jubilee Conservatory in honour of Queen Victoria's recent Diamond Jubilee. Built by James Boyd of Glasgow, this conservatory was a handsome structure, well positioned at the top of two flights of steps leading off the main avenue through the garden. The building was of moderate height, made of wood and had a central octagonal tower. It was not curvilinear. When all expenses were paid this conservatory, which was the central showpiece of the garden, cost just under £3 000, a sum which was raised mainly from public subscriptions. On 8 December 1898 the Governor, Walter Hely-Hutchinson, officially opened the building in the presence of the Mayor of Durban, John Nicol, the President of the Durban Botanic Society, Sir Benjamin Greenacre, and a large gathering of townsfolk dressed in their Sunday best. A ceremonial gold key surmounted by a *V.R.* was presented to the Governor, who proceeded to make a strong speech in support of botanical institutions in Natal as being useful for educational

BOTANICAL GARDEN, DURBAN.

The Jubilee Conservatory, erected in 1897. In the foreground is the pond built to grow the giant *Victoria amazonica* lily.
(Durban Local History Museum)

purposes and scientific research. Hely-Hutchinson, who was personally extremely interested in botany and would have done more for its advancement had it been in his power, took advantage of the grand opening to issue to the press a memorandum on the botanic gardens of Natal which had been drawn up some years before by the late Sir Theophilus Shepstone.

Although the opening of the Jubilee Conservatory cost the Society £21 it was a great festive occasion with families picnicking in the gardens and listening to the band of the Durban Light Infantry. In the succeeding years the conservatory proved to be very popular with visitors, who usually visited it first before walking round the garden. In addition to this building, 1898 saw the removal of the old wooden gate to the garden and its replacement by new wrought-iron gates with 2,8 metres (30 yards) of matching fencing. This greatly improved the entrance which had always been rather scruffy. To complete the "jubilee complex" a lily pond was built on the north side of the conservatory and in 1905 a fernery, costing £900, on the south side. The fernery was the last building project before the garden fell on hard times.

The period 1882 to 1913 marks the heyday of the Durban Botanic Garden. With a water-supply, more finance available and a larger staff, all but the upper section of the garden bordering on Currie Road was being tended. By the 1890s postcards were being produced of the paths and the vista over the garden to the sea beyond. The task of making and maintaining the garden fell mostly on the shoulders of the Kew-trained head gardener, James Wylie. Wood busied himself with the herbarium, the various building projects and the administration of the garden, but it was Wylie who worked and directed the labour force in the grounds itself. By 1898 he was in charge of all outdoor work and was responsible for much of the collecting of plants in Natal and Zululand. In recognition of his work he was given the title of Curator at the beginning of 1904 when Wood was elevated to the new post of Director. Wylie remained Curator until 1916, though in fact he had full control only after Wood relinquished the directorship in 1913.

It was claimed that Wood and Wylie built up the best collection of Asian and South American plants in Africa and certainly the garden boasted many exotic species in these later years. Wylie, like Keit, was fascinated by palms and greatly increased the garden's collection of them. He also introduced the jacaranda into South Africa from South America, the first tree flowering in 1887. A litchi tree had flowered the previous year, but the most popular exhibit was the giant *Victoria amazonica* lily, which flowered in the new lily pond in 1901. It had always been McKen's ambition to have a Victoria lily, but the promised specimen from Kew had never arrived.

The nursery lost a lot of its importance as an

experimental horticultural garden in these years, but it continued to produce large quantities of fruit and flowers for sale. The garden hosted regular flower-shows in the town during the 1880s and 1890s; the main avenue of the garden itself was noted for its spread of colourful flowers and shrubs. Strenuous efforts were made to establish a rose garden but it was only in 1887 that the problem of white ants was solved by planting the roses in large tubs. The garden's collection of fern species increased from 20 in 1880 to 160 in 1885, and of orchids from eight species in 1883 to 62 in 1887. The 1897 catalogue of plant types in the garden lists 551 names. By 1915 this number had increased to 774.

The pride of the garden's plant collection was the seven species of cycad found in the grounds, the most famous and rarest of them being discovered by Wood and named after him *Encephalartos woodii*. In 1895 while on a collecting trip with wagon and oxen in the Ngoye mountains of Zululand, Wood had discovered a clump of male plants. Some years later Wylie relocated the spot and brought several of the smaller plants back to the garden. Wood's claim that they were over 2 000 years old was exaggerated, but they were certainly several hundred years old. Wood's two original specimens were planted on either side of the path leading to the Jubilee Conservatory steps and made a very handsome addition to the conservatory complex.

As well as the plant life, the botanic garden offered the visitor a wide variety of bird and butterfly life. So prevalent did butterfly netting become in the garden that Wood was forced to restrict it to permit holders only. Not all the birds, however, were so protected. Weaver birds became such a nuisance, stealing shreds of young palms from the nursery to build their nests, that in 1900 a man was employed in the nursery to ward them off with a gun. The venture failed miserably.

The new century brought an increase in visitors, partly due to the garden's increased attractiveness, but also because the town was expanding in its general direction. Statistics of the number of visitors do not exist but the Corporation felt it worthwhile to initiate a tram service from the centre of Durban out to the garden. Trams left half-hourly and the journey cost three pence or four pence depending on where the traveller sat. Many local celebrities visited the gardens and occasionally notables from overseas did so too. As well as the Governors in the last quarter of the nineteenth and the early twentieth centuries, visitors included Lord Wolseley and his staff; Sir Bartle Frere; J. A. Froude; Lady Castletown; Secretary Swart; Marianne North; and the officers of the French warship, *Rance*.

In recognition of the growing popularity of the garden, the Botanic Society built a tea house in the form of a pagoda adjacent to Sydenham Road in 1905. A gate was opened to this road, though precautions were taken against allowing the garden

to become a pedestrian thoroughfare. The tea room was a simple construction of brick, wood and asbestos slate and sheeting. A covered verandah allowed patrons to sit under shelter and look out over the garden. The cost of construction and furniture amounted to £400. The building was rented to a Mrs and Miss Malyon who had come from the Cape. The "teas" they served between 10 a.m. and 6 p.m. were said to be of a high standard and the ginger beer was often favourably remarked upon. Comments in the visitors' book to the tea room make interesting reading:

"To visit a place like this after years of Witwatersrand life make one feel again civilized". (J. Evans, Johannesburg)

"Je ne connais qu'un site aussi magnifique que The Botanic Garden, c'est l'éclatant St. Tropez (Var) France". (Officer from *Rance*)

"The tea here is the best I have tasted south of the equator". (W. J. Ballard)

"This Tea room is like the Labour Party in Natal—just what was wanted". (J. R. Casnell, Durban)

"After wandering in many strange lands it is a glad surprise to meet with so many English and Indian friends in the trees of this garden". (Carl Mluülter, Lahore)

"I always think these gardens are the 'Kew' of Natal—after a residence of over 25 years in the town of Durban I have watched the growth of the many improvements herein". (M. Walter)

Occasionally the Botanic Society allowed a band to play in the garden on a Sunday afternoon, and this always attracted a crowd. Various ceremonies were also held in the grounds. For instance, in 1910 to mark the creation of the Union of South Africa, Wood planted four trees. In the 1890s the botanic garden was involved in the annual Arbor Days which were held in Durban and Pietermaritzburg. The garden also received publicity from its distribution of free plants to local churches, cemeteries and hospitals. It seemed as if the Durban Botanic Garden was an established institution, the pride of Natal. This was not so; as early as 1906 forces were at work which were rapidly to undermine and destroy the garden as a botanical institution.

Not every citizen in Natal was enamoured with the garden ruled over by the patriarchal Medley Wood. Wood had made enemies by his rather offhand dealing with the general public. Until old age he opposed the opening of a tea room or allowing a band into the garden. Like Keit before him, Wood was annoyed by the behaviour of many visitors to the garden. The public stole fruit, flowers and plants. They handled delicate plants, took too many butterflies and stole birds' eggs out of the garden. Fires were lit, children slid down grass banks and ran through bushes and hedges. The public destroyed benches, those that the white ants had not eaten away, and worst of all they carved their "detestable" initials on the bark of trees. Angry letters denouncing such activities regularly appeared in the local press under Wood's name.

Wood also fiercely opposed schemes to cut a road through the garden joining Botanic Gardens Road with Sydenham Road. When this was first suggested in 1898 he claimed that such an action would be a calamity which would "almost ruin" the garden. A later proposal that the tram should be allowed through the garden he also strongly opposed.

None the less many influential people felt the botanic garden did not justify the Government grant paid to it annually. Wood, they believed, must be forced to popularize the garden or be faced with it being placed in the hands of the Corporation or turned over for the use of a new country club. One detractor wrote to the press asserting, "To dub these gardens 'botanic' is absurd. But that a certain amount of original bush has been allowed to stand they would be ghastly". The strongest and most vocal of Wood's opponents were the local nurserymen, who saw the garden as being in subsidized competition with themselves. To survive, the botanic garden needed its nursery sales. In the period 1906 to 1913 sales ranged from £1 250 to £2 100 annually. A record was achieved in 1906, when in the month of October £350 worth of produce and plants was sold to the public.

The situation was a difficult one for the now aged Wood to handle. On top of external pressure on him old problems continued to return. With the Anglo-Boer war labour became scarce again. Drought occasionally recurred, as in 1899/1900 when the annual rainfall dropped to 71 cm (28 inches). The ground dried up and most of the fruit crop was lost. When the rains returned the ponds filled up and quickly became a breeding ground for mosquitoes. So serious did the problem of malaria become for Wood and his staff that £50 was spend in 1905 to fill in the lower pond. An earlier experience of using Government-supplied fish to eat mosquito larvae had yielded little result. The most serious casualty of malaria, from the point of view of the garden's upkeep, was James Wylie, who suffered from it for a long time; in 1906 Wood himself was also seriously ill with the disease.

Edwardian Durban saw the dramatic growth of the city as a tourist resort. From having only the botanic garden a generation earlier, now, thanks mainly to the work of Keit, Durban had many public pleasure parks as well as a zoo. Wood's determination not to become part of this trend and to maintain his garden as a botanical institution for the instruction of those interested in botany meant that with more and more amenities being opened to the general public the popularity of the botanic garden diminished. In a matter of a few years the number of visitors dropped so dramatically that in 1909 the Botanic Society was forced to close the tea-room as

it was being operated at a loss. Wood's explantion of this was accurate enough:

"In consequence chiefly of the great attractions of the beach, the number of visitors to the Garden has been so greatly reduced that it was found necessary to close the tea-room."

The garden was now left to Lady Greenacre and the handful of botanically minded citizens who remained loyal to the *status quo*. By 1907 a combination of economic depression and public hostility led the Government to axe its grant to the herbarium and halve the grant to the garden. General expenditure on the garden had kept pace with rising revenue over the previous 30 years. Indeed, expenditure between 1875 and 1904 had risen 10-fold to £4 000 per annum. The finances of the garden were in a precarious state and were kept balanced only by the Government grant. When the Government reduced its contribution the result was disastrous. As 75% of expenditure went on salaries and wages, Wood was forced to reduce his workforce in number as well as reducing the incomes of those remaining. On the eve of Union the grant was restored, but by then the physical appearance of the garden had greatly deteriorated.

Had the new Union Government not been so preoccupied the Durban Botanic Garden would have been eviscerated. As it was, the garden had a further three years' stay of execution before the end came. In that time conditions in the garden went from bad to worse. With decreased funds and less labour little could be done. The Jubilee Conservatory and Fernery were much in need of repair and flower-beds and labels required attention. Heavy rain in 1912 ruined many of the paths which had been constructed out of flattened ant-hills and ashes.

The Union Government finally intervened in 1913. The Colonial Herbarium was retained by the Government and placed under the Department of Agriculture, with Wood remaining as Director. By deed of transfer the garden, still under Wylie's curatorship, became the property of the Durban Corporation. Provision was made to permit the construction of a road (Edith Benson Road) and a tram-line through the garden. Henceforth the Natal Botanic Garden was to be erroneously called the Durban Municipal Botanic Garden, for despite this name it soon deteriorated into a second-rate public park and was rehabilitated only in the 1940s by Messrs Thorp and Thorns of the city's Parks Department. Its role as a proper botanic garden had, however, long since passed.

For Medley Wood the destruction of his institution was a sad blow. In his final report as its Director he wrote:

"During the thirty-one years that I have been in charge of the Gardens I can only say that having regard to the financial position of the society and other drawbacks the best has been done to make the Gardens, both from a botanical and a horticultural point of view, what a Botanical Garden should be."

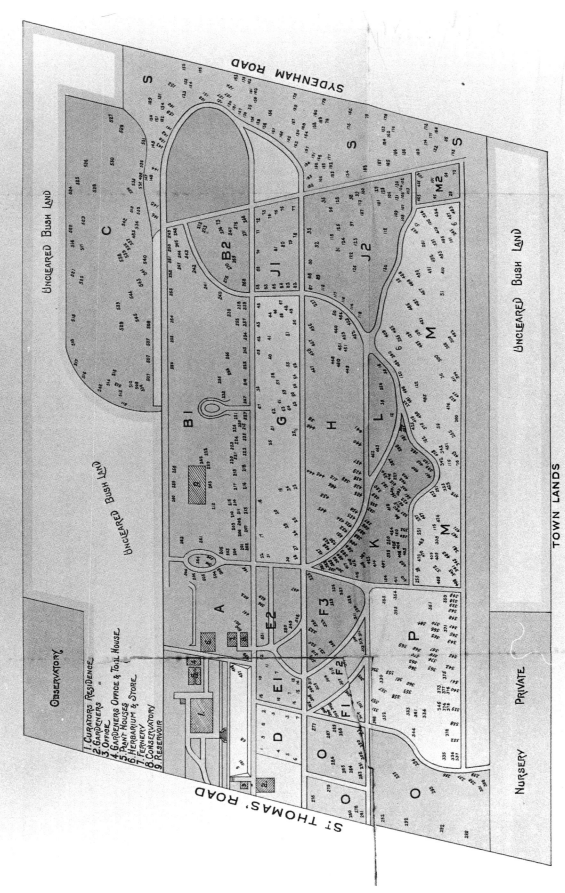

This plan of Durban Botanic Garden was included in the 1897 guide to the garden. The numbers on the map relate to items in the guide, thus visitors could easily identify plants in the grounds. (Durban Local History Museum)

With the excitement over the establishment of the National Botanic Gardens of South Africa at Kirstenbosch the fate of the Durban garden was largely irgnored. Kew, however, rallied in support of the garden it had for so long encouraged with advice and supplies of plants and seeds. In 1913 its *Kew Bulletin* noted:

"It must not be forgotten . . . that in Natal South Africa has possessed a Botanic Garden for over fifty years where the true functions of such an institution have been ably maintained in spite of many difficulties. It is a matter of regret that the area of this Garden is so small, but small though it be its maintenance is as important now as ever it was, and its activities must not be suffered to be curtailed or its functions abrogated owing to any change in its administration or to the establishment of the new National Gardens."

9 Pietermaritzburg

The establishment of a botanic garden outside Pietermaritzburg in 1874 was in response to a growing demand in the midlands of Natal for seedling trees. By the 1870s the Durban Botanic Garden was in decline but, even in more prosperous times, Durban had specialized in satisfying the Colony's horticultural needs. Little had been done to facilitate the growing and distribution of seedlings of commercially viable timber trees and fruit trees. Pietermaritzburg, situated beyond the subtropical coastal region, was eminently suited as the centre for such a project. That a garden was not established earlier was due in part to financial considerations, but also to a lack of public spirit in what many contemporaries called "sleepy hollow".

Mark McKen, the Curator of the Durban garden, encountered an apathetic response to his proposal in 1867 to create a branch of the Durban Botanic Garden in Pietermaritzburg. McKen argued that such an institution would greatly benefit the central and upper districts of Natal, and that it should specialize in arboriculture. A convenient site, he thought, could be a portion of the Pietermaritzburg public park. Admittedly some interest had been taken in experimenting with new crops by the capital's Agricultural Society in the 1850s, but this had not extended to the establishment of a botanic garden. Only in 1872 did a Botanic Society emerge with enough drive and support of such local dignitaries as Theophilus Shepstone, J. W. Akerman, J. N. Wheelen and P. C. Sutherland to initiate the establishment of a garden. Significantly this was at a time when four botanic gardens, Fort Beaufort, Port Elizabeth, Kimberley and Graaff-Reinet, had recently opened in the Cape Colony, all of these with the primary aim of providing their hinterland with seedlings.

The new Pietermaritzburg Botanic Society approached the City Council for a grant of land suitable for a botanic garden. The Council referred the matter to a Town Lands Committee. It was not until March of the following year that a site was agreed upon, and it was only on 3 March 1874 that the Council formally approved the granting of this site, in trust, to the Botanic Society. This area of town land was situated in the Zwartkop valley a couple of miles from the city. The 41 ha. (101,5 acres) was variously described as "well watered and otherwise suitable" and as "a bare piece of veldt". Half of the area, to the north-east, was hilly ground which sloped steeply up from the Dorp Spruit, then the city watercourse. The rest of the ground was fairly low-lying, but unfortunately within the frost zone. Samuel Todd, a local nurseryman, drew up the plan for the garden's layout.

The garden was administered by the council of the Botanic Society. These councillors were elected annually and usually numbered 11. The Mayors of Pietermaritzburg and Durban were *ex officio* councillors and the Government exercised the right to nominate two further councillors in view of the official grant made annually to the Society. The objectives of the Botanical Society were threefold: the growing of plants for distribution in the Colony and collecting of indigenous plants for exchange; the growing of economically viable vegetable products suitable for the upper and central districts of Natal; and the accumulation of plants of value, beauty and rarity in the Society's garden.

The income of the Society came from three principal sources. The annual Government grant, which remained a constant £350, was occasionally supplemented by a Pietermaritzburg Corporation grant. These monies were generally less than £100 per annum and infrequently granted; only in 1906 and 1907 when the Corporation donated £700 and £350 respectively was this source of income of any significant benefit to the garden. Until the turn of the century official grants usually constituted over 70% of the Society's total income. The remaining £100 to £200 was raised from sales from the nursery or through subscriptions. Companies and individuals who paid one guinea a year to become subscribers had the right to enter the garden on the two weekdays it was closed to the general public and to reclaim their subscription at the nursery in plants to the value of their donation. It was a system which never attracted many people. In 1876 there were 35 subscribers; in 1880 the number had risen to 114, but three years later it had dropped to 72 and by 1889 it stood at 26 subscribers contributing a mere 7% of revenue. This figure was to rise slightly in the Edwardian period, but it never surpassed 20% in the period under survey.

The total annual revenue of the Pietermaritzburg Botanic Garden exceeded £1 000 only in 1904 and 1906, and was generally considerably lower than its counterpart in Durban. This position could have been altered had not the founders of the Society clung to their policy of supplying the central and upper region of Natal with a plentiful amount of cheap or free seedlings. The relatively small sums raised annually from sales, usually under 20% of total income, present a false picture. For years the Pietermaritzburg garden distributed thousands of young plants annually in an attempt to encourage the planting of trees. A large number of trees were distributed free to Government and public institutions. Churches, hospitals, the railway and cemeteries all benefited from the Society's generosity, and those plants which were sold barely covered the nursery expenses in their rearing. For example, in

A general view over Pietermaritzburg botanic garden.
(Killie Campbell Africana Library, Durban)

1888 over 10 000 plants and shrubs were sold to the public for only £68, and in 1911 the military establishment at Fort Napier was provided with a large number of trees, shrubs, palms, hedge plants, bedding plants and lawn grass, all for the meagre sum of £38.

After 1910 a new policy of vigorously exploiting sales to the full was adopted which resulted in a three-fold rise in sales between then and 1929. This action, plus the decision to sell plants and flowers on a Sunday, led to an outcry in the press and the garden was accused of "violating the fundamental principles that ought to govern a botanical insitution". In the period 1874 to 1910, however, no substantial returns came from the vast output of the botanic garden's nursery.

The meagre income of the Botanic Society had several unfortunate consequences. The *Natal Witness* noted "no botanist would accept a curatorship for the salary offered". This stood at £200 per annum, having remained at £175 for many years. The *Witness'* comment was not completely accurate, for Pietermaritzburg had a series of fine Curators, three of whom, Messrs Hislop, Marriott and Newberry were Kew-trained men and of a high professional quality. Nevertheless, because the salary was so low, curators rarely remained in the gardens long before they were tempted away by nurserymen or by more lucrative employment at another botanical institution. In the 36 years from 1874 to 1910 there

were some eight full-time Curators and several caretakers. Only the first Curator, E. Willis, and the fourth, G. Mitchell, were established long enough in the garden to undertake and see through major developments.

A second consequence of the scarcity of funds was that a proper botanic garden was not laid out at the start with plants grouped according to family. None the less, Pietermaritzburg was better managed than most South African botanic gardens of the period in that Willis, and after him T. Harris and R. W. Adlam, did create what was in effect an arboretum. The hill land was planted with varieties of conifers and the lower part laid out in geometrical form with blocks of tightly packed specimens of timber trees. Only in 1894 did Mitchell lay a proper path to connect these two halves of the garden and by so doing permit the public to walk to the summit where, it was claimed, one had the "best view in southern Africa". The path also helped labourers carrying water up to the plantation trees. Alexander Hislop was of the opinion in 1905 that it would have been a much better plan to have sited the whole garden on the hill. However, with his departure for England in 1906, nothing further was done to landscape this upper portion of the garden, though in 1910 some of the black wattle growing there was cleared away.

The section of the garden lying beneath the hill in the valley was not altered dramatically until

Mitchell's curatorship (1889–1900). Prior to his arrival efforts were concentrated on building up compartments, each closely packed with one species of tree. The nursery was also very important, being an extensive affair and very much the centre of activity in the garden. In 1883 one of the Government nominees on the Society's council wrote scathingly about this to the Colonial Secretary of Natal. Pietermaritzburg Botanic Garden, he claimed, was without shelter and was in reality a nursery. He continued:

> "The time has arrived when a decided step in advance should be made; the nursery should be given up, and the time, labour, and money expended in the introduction and growing of fresh examples of Botanical interest, as also in cultivating as wide a range as possible of medicinal plants."

This was not entirely fair criticism: for the tree enthusiast and plantation owner there was much of interest. The attractions for the general public were two tree-lined "walks". One, called the Hakea Walk, was 114 metres (380 feet) in length and survived until 1899 when its trees fell victim to age, the white ants and the determination of Mitchell to root out as many trees as possible. The second walk was initially outside the Society's grounds, but jointly maintained by the Society and the local Corporation. This was the Mayor's Walk. Originating in 1876 from a footpath, it was lined with many oaks. By the late 1880s these had given way mainly to cypresses, pines and types of acacia and casuarina. Pleasant as these walks were, the garden boasted few flower-beds and herbaceous borders. Indeed, in the first 15 years of its existence little was done to beautify the garden or encourage visitors. Though in the first six years the average number of annual visitors doubled from approximately 400 to 860, by 1885 the figure had dropped to just under 600 where it remained for the rest of the 1880s. With such modest support it is surprising that in 1879 the Society went to the expense of erecting turnstiles at the entrances to the gardens.

The public image of the garden had never been glowing and in 1883 it was further tarnished by a financial scandal which for a time threatened the garden's future. The sudden death of the Society's treasurer led to the uncovering of a fraud. From November 1881 on he had misappropriated a sizeable proportion of the Society's income. Unfortunately, the auditors had failed to examine all the Society's financial papers and at the end of 1882 had pronounced a debit balance of £63, when in actual fact the Society owed the Natal Bank alone £272. It was eventually discovered that £360 of Society money was missing. All work in the garden had to cease and large quantities of timber had to be cut down to pay off the debt; £246 was raised in this fashion. The Society was saved from insolvency by the Pietermaritzburg Corporation which granted them a loan of £350 at 6% interest in January 1884. To prevent a recurrence of such a disaster the

Botanic Society from then on insisted on their treasurer's depositing a £200 security bond on accepting office.

Only slightly less embarrassing was the discovery in the 1880s that for some years the Society had been using non-standard meteorological instruments in the botanic garden, so that the method of taking the readings was inaccurate. As a result the observation readings were described in a forestry report in 1889 as "useless". The meteorological observations continued to be a subject of considerable dispute for many years and as late as 1905 the instruments were being "readjusted" to satisfy hostile criticism in the local press.

As the 1880s progressed the various Curators began to concern themselves more with the study of botany and the establishment of an attractive garden. A little collecting of plant specimens was carried on, mainly locally, and correspondence was entered into with Kew. Revenue remained fairly stable at around £450 per annum, about half that of the Durban Botanic Garden. Expenditure was kept well within the annual budget. By the time Mitchell took over the curatorship the garden was considerably run down. Even the nursery, which had been its backbone, was in a sorry state and contained only nine potted plants. Speaker Akerman, the President of the Botanic Society, described Mitchell on his appointment as being "able and zealous". Certainly Mitchell was to do for the Pietermaritzburg Botanic Garden what Wood had done for the Durban one.

The nursery was rehabilitated to its former glory. In 1891, thanks to a Government grant of £250, a small iron green-house was constructed, the first in the garden. It was to prove a considerable success. The plants within it were said to grow in a most "luxuriant and remarkable manner". Two years later a fernery was built in the nursery. This was converted into a propagating house some years later and it was not until 1910 that a new fernery was constructed.

So successful was the nursery that it received considerable publicity, much of it hostile from competing local commercial nurserymen. Not only were seedlings sold or given from it, but Mitchell initiated several afforestation schemes in the surrounding district. He actively encouraged the Natal Government to establish a Department of Forestry and offered them part of his garden as an experimental station for such a department. In 1893 he himself established an experimental orchard, which was to become famous for the astonishing variety of European, American and Asian fruit trees it contained.

The task of rehabilitating the rest of the garden was more difficult and took much longer. Four years after Mitchell's appointment the Governor of Natal, Hely-Hutchinson, wrote to Kew of the Pietermaritzburg Botanic Garden:

> "It is a pretty place, with great possibilities: but it gives

me the impression of not having had a very lively interest taken in it, and there were many things which I should have liked to make observations about if I had the same powers which I had in the West Indies."

Mitchell was not daunted by the task which confronted him. His services to public institutions and to surrounding towns made him a well-known figure. For example, he advised the Pietermaritzburg Corporation on the eradication of caterpillars from the many oak trees which lined the capital's streets and he planted 50 *Pinus radiata* and 50 *P. pinaster* around the market square in Stanger. His principal concern was, however, to improve the appearance of the botanic garden. To raise capital for this he allowed the Natal Government Railway to build a line into the botanic garden right up to the hillside, where a quarry was opened to extract ballast for the new Greytown line at a cost of three pence per cubic yard. In the Edwardian period sand was also sold from the garden at a shilling a load.

One of the main problems with the Pietermaritzburg Botanic Garden, according to Mitchell, was the excessive number of trees, which exhausted the soil. Following the advice of Medley Wood, who held that a botanic garden needed only three of any one species of plant or tree, unless an experiment was being carried on, in 1896 a massive thinning scheme was undertaken. This continued right through until 1910. The work was contracted out and numerous wagonloads of timber made their way from the garden to the town for auction. In place of the plantations grass was sown and flower-beds and herbaceous borders were laid out. In 1905 Alexander Hislop stated that this policy had altered the character of the garden by making it look bigger and opening up new vistas. Unfortunately Mitchell's concern to improve the image of the botanic garden led him to commence establishing what was to become, as the years passed, more and more of a pleasure park. He did not take the opportunity provided by his reorganization to establish a proper botanic garden.

A programme of building was initiated after 1889. In 1890 a substantial house for the curator was erected which contained a small library. At first surrounded by trees, in 1898 these were cut down and replaced by grass. Several bridges were constructed. The wooden bridges either rotted or were washed away in floods and were eventually replaced by brick culverts. An attempt to fence the ground met with only limited success. Cattle trespassing and eating young shoots and plants had for long been a problem, but fencing rarely lasted long as it was either stolen or washed away.

The damming of the stream into a pond or small lake met with more success. The Society then offered the use of the pond in 1890 to the Government for "the promotion of pisciculture". The offer was not taken up, but instead the pond was stocked with waterlilies, geese and four swans. In 1898 three of the swans were killed one night by a wild animal and it was another three years before a Durban gentleman replenished the stock with a gift of two black swans. The pond proved very popular with the public and it was found profitable to replace the adjacent summer-house with a tea-room, which opened at weekends and on public holidays. The only problem with the pond was that it often filled up with soil and rock. This was solved to some extent in 1894 when its sides were raised by 0,3 metre (one foot), but then the water became covered with algae slime. Ten years later attempts to clear this were still failing to produce satisfactory results.

During the 1890s further amenities were added. Paths of shale were laid down throughout the garden and arches and wattle shelters were erected. A drinking fountain was placed in a central spot. A number of potting sheds and tool houses were put up, and accommodation quarters for the labouring staff were built.

The growing of flowers took on importance and from 1892 onwards the Society exhibited at local flower-shows. A rockery was established the following year and a prize collection of azaleas grown. Cut flowers were sold to the public and many institutions such as the Victoria Club had a regular order with the garden. Further stimulus to attendance figures was given by the Arbor Days which were held under the garden's sponsorship from 1889. In 1894 the first catalogue of plants in the garden was printed to supplement the labels, which in 1901 had to be placed out of the reach of children.

The public were particularly encouraged to visit the garden on public holidays and on special occasions. A large crowd was present in April 1891 when President Kruger planted a japonica in the garden. Similarly, on a less formal occasion in 1910, the garden was full when the officers of the local barracks treated the ranks and their families to a picnic in the grounds. Bands were hired, usually once a month, to play in the new bandstand and on public holidays marquees were often erected.

With the garden becoming increasingly popular, the Botanic Society was in a position to pressurize the Corporation to provide improved communications between town and the garden. The Zwartkop Road was a dirt road which, it was claimed, one could paddle along on a boat when it rained. The footpath to the garden from the top of Church Street was equally unsatisfactory in wet weather thanks to the military riding their horses over it. Only in 1899 did the Corporation finally agree to harden Zwartkop Road as well as the Mayor's Walk. The principal entrance was now from Mayor's Walk and a new piece of road was constructed to connect it with Zwartkop Road. The old entrance with its dilapidated wooden bridge and unsightly labourers' accommodation was closed. The Mayor's Walk was further altered in 1907 when at the suggestion of the

The curator's house, erected in 1890.
(Killie Campbell Africana Library, Durban)

Governor an avenue of plane trees was planted to create a majestic entrance to the gardens.

As for public transport, rickshaws could carry one to the garden, but the return fare was an expensive three shillings. Only in 1906, when a tram-line was constructed which terminated at the botanic garden, was this expense dramatically lowered. The return journey on the tram cost a mere eight pence. In 1904 Hislop remarked,

"Owing to its isolated position the botanic gardens have never found much favour with the public as a place of resort, except on special holidays, when they feel the extravagance of a conveyance warranted."

The tram was to alter this and on Michaelmas Day 1907 the garden was filled by several thousand visitors. Not that the previous numbers of visitors had been low. Once Mitchell began to popularize the garden in the 1890s the numbers increased dramatically. For example, in September 1891 there were well over 800 visitors, the number which a few years before would have come in one year. In 1893 it was normal to have between 200 and 300 visitors per day during ordinary holiday periods.

The consequences of an increase in public interest in the garden were not all good. Much damage was done. In 1893 it took the entire staff three hours to extinguish a grass fire. This was not the first fire which was suspected of being maliciously started. In 1901 the Society was forced to request police patrols in the garden and in 1904 so much damage was being done and so many thefts had occurred that the Society prosecuted six offenders, all of whom were convicted. New bye-laws restricting times of entry and prohibiting children from entering unaccompanied only had a limited effect.

The Curator's problems were not limited to a destructive public. Flooding was a regular occurrence. The worst example of this was on 3 January 1895. The Curator's diary noted:

"A great flood came down in the afternoon doing a great deal of damage. Amongst other things it washed the summer-house down by the banks of the lake, washed out a number of trees and shrubs and almost filled the lake with soil. Washed down a good deal of the fence which was put up last winter, also all the fence at the bottom of the garden. Washed out several of the fruit trees from the orchard, and an immense quantity of soil and left the lower-lying portions of the gardens covered with debris."

Bad winters in 1893 and 1898 killed off many plants including many of the garden's palms. A hail-storm in 1905 devastated the nursery, and 7 degrees of frost on one night of the following year further reduced its output.

Related to weather was plant disease, and for several years Mitchell attempted to find a solution which would kill apple-leaf blight. Sheep dip helped a little, but it was only in 1894 that Mitchell could claim to have found a satisfactory mixture. This was a solution of sulphur, quick-lime, soft soap and paraffin. A more potent mixture was discovered to kill off the ever-troublesome white ants, which by 1896 had destroyed every seat in the garden and many young plants. It was found, however, that the solution killed plants as well as ants, so it could be used only on benches and dead trees. In 1901 the seating problem was solved by the railways presenting the garden with a considerable number of iron benches. The extensive use of straw manure from the mule-train yard was said to encourage the presence of ants, but alternative supplies of manure were extremely hard to obtain.

None of these problems was as serious for the everyday running of the garden as that of the periodic shortage of labour. Until 1898 black labour was employed to help the Curator and his assistant. Thirty blacks were employed during 1891, but never more than 13 at any one time. Only one labourer worked for more than eight months in the year. Monthly wages varied between 9 shillings and one pound, but most earned between 18 shillings and a pound a month. Three years later the total number of black labourers employed was 16, with never more than eight working at once. Two of these, however, were permanent. Wages were similar to those of 1891.

As the activities of the garden expanded more labour was required. Labourers were needed for watering, weeding and especially for cutting grass by hand. Only in 1910 was a mowing machine purchased, and even then it constantly broke down and the old method had to be employed. Labour was also needed in the nursery, watering and transplanting, and in the orchard, budding, grafting and generally attending to the fruit trees.

Following Wood's advice, Mitchell employed an unspecified number of non-indentured free Indians. The scheme failed, however, for Mitchell was not prepared to allow his new employees to work a nine and a half hour day, from 7.30 a.m. to 5 p.m. This, he claimed, caused unrest among his black labourers who worked from sunrise to sunset. The Indians left, much to Mitchell's relief. He said he preferred black labourers; some of those he employed had, he said, worked in the garden off and on for many years, "and might almost be classed as skilled labour".

By 1901 Mitchell was dead and the Anglo-Boer War was being waged within 80 kms (50 miles) of the garden. The war meant that the garden under its new Curator, George Robertson, was very short of labour. It was therefore decided to revert to the 1898 policy of employing Indian labour. Within a few years the Indian workforce was installed in new accommodation and was being praised for its superior reliability over that of the black, "whose frequent visits to his kraal make him a very unreliable labourer". These workers were supplemented in 1907 by the use of convict labour in the garden.

The 1906/7 depression in Natal hit the Pietermaritzburg Botanic Garden badly, and for a while only maintenance work was carried on. The Curator, W. E. Marriott, coped with the situation very well. With the assistance of W. J. Newberry he was able to revive the garden as Mitchell had done in the early 1890s, and by planting numerous shrubs and laying

The lawn and plane avenue.
(Killie Campbell Africana Library, Durban)

out new flower-beds increase its beauty. On 11 October 1907 the *Natalian* lauded his work with these words:

> "The great improvements that have taken place in the last two years are rapidly raising the Garden to a position second to none in South Africa, and it is a matter for amazement that so much could have been accomplished in so short a time . . . a veritable lung of the city, soothing to the eye and brain, and appealing to the sense of all that is beautiful and good and noble."

1907 also saw one of Marriott's Lycopodia win a diploma of merit at the South African Products Exhibition in London. The plant was later given to Kew.

The Pietermaritzburg Botanic Garden did not suffer the fate of the Durban Botanic Garden in being taken over by the local Municipality. Only in 1969 did it pass into the hands of the National Botanic Gardens of South Africa. The popularizing of the garden, in the 1890s and the production of cheap seedlings to satisfy demand placed the garden in a much stronger position than Durban, which made little concession to public opinion. Attempts in Pietermaritzburg to establish a more scientifically based botanic garden had come to little. Collecting trips were amateurish. Mitchell's account of one in 1895 went as follows:

> "Walked to Zwaartkop on a botanizing expedition. On arrival was dead beat—and by the time I was rested it was time to come back."

Occasionally plants were exchanged with other botanical institutions, but little could be sent as by the Curator's own admission there was not much that was exciting or indigenous in the garden. From 1898 onwards Medley Wood was consulted and he was paid three guineas annually to visit the garden. As far as the exchange of plants was concerned, his advice was to make sure the garden knew the proper name of a plant before sending it labelled to another botanical institution. Incorrect labelling had, he said, given Natal "rather a bad name".

In 1893 there had been talk of establishing a herbarium but nothing came of it, mainly for financial reasons. Where the Society did try hard to make progress was in the establishment of a section of the garden devoted to indigenous plants. An area at the foot of the hill was cleared for this purpose in 1893 and in the following year seeds of indigenous trees were sown. Most of these were washed away in the 1895 flood. By 1898 nothing of the experiment remained, so Mitchell appealed to forest plantation owners and farmers in Natal to send him samples of indigenous plants from their lands. A plot was once more laid out. Only two individuals responded to the Curator's request and the two plants they sent were dead on arrival at the garden.

During the opening years of the new century there were plans to revive this scheme, but it was only when outsiders came to the Society's aid that anything was achieved. Messrs. Sim and Stayner built up a collection of tree ferns in the garden and Wood donated a collection of cacti, aloes, bamboo and grasses to the Pietermaritzburg Botanic Garden. A pharmaceutical plot was not laid out until 1913, though such a venture had been discussed for 20 years.

The heyday of the Pietermaritzburg Botanic Garden was yet to come. In common with so many of South Africa's botanic gardens by the end of the colonial era it was little more than an attractive pleasure park containing some interesting foreign trees and a commercial nursery: a far cry from the later description of it given by Sir Frederick Keeble in the 1930s,

> "An ideal Botanical Garden: the Pride of Natal—and of Kew."

10 The impact of the botanic gardens on the economy of Natal

When the Natal Agricultural and Horticultural Society was formed in 1848 the Colony of Natal was still in its infancy. Economically it was a time of great uncertainty. Ivory, skins and wool were exported but no single agricultural crop dominated farming. During the 1850s and 1860s a large number of crops were tried most of which proved to be unsuitable climatically, or too labour-intensive, or generally unviable economically due to marketing and distribution problems.

At the centre of this process of trial and experiment, and encouraged in this regard by the Colonial Government, was the Durban Botanic Garden. The role of the garden in the 1850s and 1860s was three-fold. It acted as a distribution centre for agricultural plants and seeds. Statistics covering these early years do not exist but by the 1870s thousands of plants and hundreds of packets of seeds were being distributed annually to farmers and planters, usually free of charge on application to the curator. Ornamental trees and shrubs, fruit and flowers were, however, usually sold.

Closely allied to the garden's role as the distribution centre for plants and seeds was its function as an unofficial place of quarantine, at least until effective regulations were promulgated in 1881. It was normal for live plants and seeds to be taken from the ships in Durban harbour to the garden prior to distribution.

Of greater consequence than either of these two, however, was the botanic garden's role as the young Colony's agricultural crop research station. The garden encouraged the growing in Natal of as wide a variety of commercial plants as possible. To promote this policy, the Horticultural Society held annual functions, the first being on 9 August 1850. The first exhibition of colonial produce was a failure despite the offering of prizes. Two months later, however, the arrival in the Colony of Mark McKen, who soon became Curator of the Durban Botanic Garden, marked the beginning of significant changes in Natal agriculture. He brought with him a large number of new plants which had been entrusted to him by Sir William Hooker of Kew and which included:

> Allspice, rose apple, arrowroot, breadfruit, cocoa, camphor, cinnamon, coffee, gamboge, ginger, guava, jackfruit, longaan, loquat, mango, blood and mandarin orange, pawpaw, black pepper, quassia, Assam and Paraguay tea and wampee.

McKen's achievements as Curator were mixed, as we have seen. He failed to make much headway with laying out the grounds; indeed in the mid-1850s only some 2,4 ha. (six acres) of bush had been cleared to establish what was in effect an allotment plot. On the other hand, he was energetic in his research. He resigned his position in 1853, but returned again in 1860 and remained until his death in April 1872. In the interim the garden suffered through a lack of continuity of staff. This did not, however, lead to a cessation either of experiments or of the shows, which were held in the garden from 1851 onwards and which quickly became an established annual holiday for the town. By 1859 three silver cups were being offered as prizes for various agricultural exhibits.

The Durban Botanic Garden was responsible for disseminating many of the crop plants which were to pull Natal out of subsistence agriculture, but it also had a restricting influence on agricultural activity. Such species as the rubber plant, *Hevea brasiliensis*, hops and the opium poppy, *Papaver somniferum*, were considered unsuitable for Natal and their growing was discouraged. The garden was not always successful in its campaigns to popularize certain species and occasionally met with apathy from the farming community.

The plight of nineteenth century Natal agriculture might have been less dire had the attempts of the garden to encourage the growing of new commercial plants been more successful. For example, in the early 1850s the garden tried to promote the establishment of silk cultivation in Natal. Silkworm eggs were imported from Cape Town and 120 white mulberry plants were laid out in a 0,6 ha. (1,5 acre) plot in the garden. By 1852 a thousand mulberry plants had been produced. Nothing came of the venture due to a lack of public enthusiasm.

Later, in the 1860s, McKen tried to promote the widespread growing of the quinine-yielding plant, *Cinchona succirubra*. Plants offered free to farmers elicited only 32 applications. Much publicity was given to the promulgation of fibrous grasses, especially China grass, or *Boehmeria nivea*: the response was equally poor. Not only did farmers very often fail to heed the advice given by curators in their annual reports, in public newspapers and in the *Government Gazette*, but they also rarely responded to requests for progress reports on plants provided to them by the garden. Their attitude seriously hampered the garden's effectiveness and exposed it to unfair public criticism. In fact, the Durban Botanic Garden was a boon to the new Colony for it was the principal publicist of six major commercial crops—arrowroot, cotton, tobacco, tea, coffee and sugar-cane—some of which were to prove the salvation of Natal agriculture.

Arrowroot was McKen's first successful venture. Within a year of his arrival in Natal he had raised about a hectare (a third of an acre) of it from the single *Maranta arundinacea* plant he had brought with him from Kew. Plants were distributed to applicants and a special arrowroot prize was introduced at the Horticultural Society's annual show. By 1861 the prize was £5, a considerable sum and an indication of the great hopes invested in this would-be saviour of the wavering Natal economy. The enterprise was to fail due to the poor prices fetched by the commodity. Despite its suitability for the climate and soil conditions the amount of arrowroot grown in Natal declined rapidly in the 1860s. So successfully had it flourished, however, that in 1901 Wood, then Curator of the Durban Botanic Garden, pressed vigorously for its re-adoption as a staple Natal crop.

Another crop heavily promoted by the botanic garden but likewise destined to be undercut by declining world prices was cotton. The red hill soil of the Berea proved most successful for the growing of both Sea Island and New Orleans cotton plants. McKen and the Horticultural Society were even more enthusiastic about the prospects of cotton than they were about arrowroot and offered a spectacular prize of £10 at the annual show for the best cotton exhibit. This was to be the largest amount of prize money ever offered at the shows. Imported cottons and the indigenous *Gossypium herbaceum* were to prove of only mediocre quality and it was not until the American Civil War in the 1860s disrupted supply to the Lancashire mills that cotton cultivation expanded in Natal. Unfortunately, during these years the plant fell victim to attack by red spiders. The slump of 1870 in cotton growing was not as dramatic as has been supposed. In that year the botanic garden sold a large quantity of cotton seed supplied by the Cotton Supply Association of Manchester. By July the President of the Natal Agricultural and Horticultural Society, John Sanderson, was able to announce that the garden had 10 hundredweight of cotton seed left to distribute as well as pamphlets on cotton cultivation. Cotton was never to become a large export crop because of foreign competition, but it continued to be grown in many small pockets in the Natal midlands and north coast regions for purely domestic reasons. The Durban garden, and later the Pietermaritzburg garden, periodically experimented with new strains. As late as 1905 T. R. Sim, the former Curator of the King Williams Town Botanic Garden and now the Conservator of Natal Forests, noted that the two patches of cotton in the Pietermaritzburg Botanic Garden were the finest in Natal—more healthy and vigorous than the plots in the coastal experimental farm and much superior to that being tried in Zululand.

Like cotton, tobacco proved suitable for growing in Natal and though never grown on an extensive scale it was successful, especially as a smallholder's crop. Tobacco growing at the garden began in 1851 and as early as October of the following year specimens of savannah tobacco were being supplied to the Pietermaritzburg Agricultural Society. The first issue of the *Natal Mercury* (25 November 1852) announced that tobacco was available from the Durban garden. Although the garden supplied a small amount of tobacco seeds to farmers in the 1860s it was not until the 1870s that demand for them became noticeable. The Durban Curator, William Keit, appealed to Kew several times in 1873 for tobacco seeds but the seed did not arrive until March 1875. His successor, Medley Wood, was surprised at the demand for tobacco. He was more specific in his request to Kew, asking for superior varieties which could be used in the production of cigars and cigarettes. He noted:

"Hitherto the chief aim of growers has been to grow those kinds of coarse tobacco which would produce as heavy crop, for sale chiefly to natives, but since so many free coolies have engaged in its cultivation the price has fallen so low that it will not pay Europeans to produce it." [K.C. 1740]

Kew's response was to provide Wood with 30 different varieties which he distributed among planters. Wood believed that even good quality tobacco would have difficulty in competing with foreign produce and that to establish a domestic tobacco industry would involve expenditure on the construction of a manufacturing plant far beyond the resources of a Colony on the brink of penury. None the less both the Durban and, later, the Pietermaritzburg Botanic Gardens strove to improve the quality to tobacco grown in Natal. By 1906 Pietermaritzburg was offering farmers a choice of 15 types of tobacco seed.

The Durban Botanic Garden was similarly used as an entrepôt for the distribution of tea to planters, especially during the last quarter of the nineteenth century. Hulett and the major Natal tea-planters had direct links with Kew, the Indian tea-planters and Indian botanical institutions. Their desire was to introduce and popularize the best Assam teas as well as pekoe, the scented black China tea. They were contemptuous of the "worst kind of China teas" which the garden had introduced in previous years and which by the late 1880s it was selling at "absurdly low prices". Although this was largely true and although Natal teas had on the whole been usable only as a "mixer", in 1875 and again in 1877 a large number of good quality hybrid Assam plants were received in the garden from Kew and from the Royal Botanic Garden in Calcutta. Unfortunately, few of the plants from Kew survived the journey with the result that until the early 1880s tea plants were scarce. By then the Durban Botanic Garden was not over-zealous in its promotion of tea planting, an attitude shared by the Natal Government.

The two crops with which the Durban Botanic Garden was most concerned were coffee and sugar. Unlike tea, demand for coffee outstripped world production for much of the mid-nineteenth century. By the 1890s producers could expect a shilling per pound weight, though there was upwards of a three-year delay in Natal before bushes produced beans and provided a financial return. Conditions on the Natal coast appeared suitable, especially in areas which were well sheltered and had rich deep soil.

In the early 1850s the Durban Botanic Garden was growing both Arabica and Bourbon coffee and prizes for coffee exhibits were being awarded at the Horticultural Society's annual show. In 1861 one of the new silver cup trophies was awarded for coffee. It was first won by A. McArthur. It was not until the 1870s, however, that widespread interest was taken in coffee production.

William Keit was especially concerned with the problem of coffee growing in Natal and carried on a correspondence with Sir Joseph Hooker at Kew on the matter. By 1875 it appeared that either because of failure to germinate or because of plant disease coffee had failed in the Colony. Coffee planters appealed to Kew for new varieties of coffee plant to be imported from South America. Kew's response was to dispatch a Wardian case of plants to the Durban garden. Of these, Liberian coffee initially seemed to thrive. Within two years, however, problems were being experienced with its cultivation. In his annual report Keit observed:

> "I am sorry to observe that some of the leaves are affected with *Strigula feei*, and should this kind of coffee be liable to the attacks of that parasite in the same degree as our tea plants, Magnolias, Ficus and other imported and indigenous evergreen trees, I fear that the prospect of its successful cultivation will be greatly impaired, as the vigour of the plants depends mainly on the healthy development of the leaves."

By the early 1880s the caterpillar threat to coffee leaves had diminished only to be replaced by the ravages of a fungal disease. In 1880 and again in 1884 coffee plants were attacked by the *Hemiteia* fungus which had struck the coffee plantations in both Ceylon (Sri Lanka) and Java (Djawa, Indonesia). The Government called upon Medley Wood, Keit's successor, to suggest means of eradication. The 1880 outbreak was identified by Wood as *Hemiteia vastatrix* but in 1884 he identified a new strain which was named *Hemiteia woodii*. In co-operation with Professor MacOwan of the Cape Town Botanic Garden, Wood set about trying to eradicate the disease. Aided by Government finance, Wood initiated a policy of destroying crops infected by the fungus and of cutting down wild medlar trees, which he believed to be fungus carriers. He was only partially successful in his endeavours though he was hopeful for the ultimate success of coffee in inland Natal.

Both the Durban and the Pietermaritzburg Botanic Gardens raised coffee plants for distribution, despite the problem of frost in the latter garden. By the 1890s the *Hemiteia* was less virulent and in the early years of the new century Wood experimented with *Coffea* var. *maragogipe* and *Coffea zanguebaria zanguebariae*, which appeared to be immune from disease but the beans were of a very poor quality, fetching only three pence per pound. It was not until 1905 that Wood decided that coffee was not a suitable crop because Natal was just not tropical enough.

It was in the introduction and distribution of sugar-cane that the Durban Botanic Garden was especially successful. Sugar exports from Natal rarely rose above a third of total exports but sugar none the less took a firm hold on coastal agriculture —although it was not until in the twentieth century that it really flourished. From the early 1850s the Durban garden was the focus for the development of this industry. Edmund Morewood's pioneering experiment in cane growing at Compensation Flats was in many respects a joint venture with the Curator of the Durban Botanic Garden at the time, Mark McKen. McKen had managed the Golden Grove sugar estate at Port Morant in Jamaica from 1840 until 1849. In 1850 he had come to Natal specifically to grow cane or cotton rather than with the intention of running a botanic garden. McKen not only advised Morewood and the early planters but was their principal publicist. He did more than anyone to promote the growing of sugar-cane in the coastal region and in the interval between his two stints as Curator (1853–1860) he managed Chiappini sugar estate at Tongaat.

The premier silver cup awarded by the Horticultural Society was for cane, its first recipient being F. Ferreira. In an attempt to find some means of breaking the economic depression of the late 1860s, McKen visited Pamplemousses, the botanic garden on the island of Mauritius, in 1867. It was not until 1871, however, that 22 new varieties of cane arrived from the island and were planted out in the garden. These included the China cane which was to be important during the 1870s and early 1880s. Previous to its importation no single variety had proved satisfactory. The indigenous Natal Green was widely grown, but other varieties such as Batavia, Bourbon, Creole and Ribbon were grown as well.

It was following the receipt of Keit's reports in the mid-1870s that Kew realised the potential of sugar-cane for Natal. They sent two large consignments of cane plants to the botanic garden for distribution. The first, containing 96 varieties, had unfortunately been over-watered and a third of the plants was already rotten on arrival at Durban. Only six varieties were to survive and these were dispatched to Ralph Clarence's Clare Estate. The following year a consignment of 60 varieties of cane arrived safely and was planted out in the garden.

All was not well with cane growing despite the attempts of curators to educate farmers in its cultivation. A depression in the industry was exacerbated by an outbreak of cane smut, or *Ustilago sacchari*. Wood investigated the phenomenon, as he had the outbreak of coffee-leaf disease. It is interesting to note that Kew had never heard of *Ustilago* attacking sugar-cane before.

Wood's solution once again was to uproot and destroy infected crops. He also urged diversification away from China cane to other varieties such as Bois Rouge, Elephant, Gold Dust, Port MacKay, White Tanna and Uba. Gradually Uba was to predominate and by the 1890s it constituted the back-bone of the industry, despite the fact that its sucrose content was fairly low and it was difficult to mill. The credit for its introduction, from either India or Mauritius, is usually given to Daniel de Pass, but according to Wood it was he who saved a few Uba plants from rotting in a shed at the harbour and took them to the botanic garden where they were cultivated. Whatever the truth of this, the Durban Botanic Garden certainly raised and distributed large quantities of Uba cane to planters' associations.

The second facet of the economic role of Natal's botanic gardens concerned the growing and distribution of fruit and timber trees. McKen's argument in 1867 for the establishment of a branch botanic garden in Pietermaritzburg was that it could be used for the acclimatization of European fruit trees and other trees suited to the climate of that region. When the Pietermaritzburg Botanic Garden was eventually established in 1874 it set about fulfilling this aim. In the early years it had to contend with the difficulty of obtaining seedlings. Varieties of pine and *Acacia melanoxylon* (blackwood), which was then much in demand, were costing £8 per 100 seedlings and wattle seeds were having to be "doled out in ounce packets with parsimonious care". In spite of this the garden proved very successful in promoting tree-planting in the Colony. In 1880 it offered the planter five varieties of eucalyptus, five of pine, three of cypress and two of acacia, including *A. mearnsii* (black wattle). Kew was impressed by the efforts made to ensure a supply of valuable timber for the Colony in the future and Sir Joseph Hooker went so far as to express his opinion that in this direction "Natal may be held up as a model to other colonies".

By the late 1880s the Pietermaritzburg Botanic Garden was offering seedlings to the public in sufficient quantities to "cover thousands of acres". It was not without justification that the Pietermaritzburg Botanic Society claimed in 1891:

"The Gardens have been the Forestry Department for the uplands and midlands districts of the colony for years."

In the late 1880s and early 1890s the Pietermaritzburg Botanic Garden nursery produced upwards of 20 000 plants, trees and shrubs annually. Trees which were sold at very low prices to the public constituted over 60% of this figure; a further 30% was donated to public institutions, parks and churches; and the remainder was either given to subscribers or planted out in the garden. Acacias, pines, eucalypti and cypresses were still the primary requirements of applicants for seedlings.

The Pietermaritzburg Botanic Garden also special-ized in producing fruit trees and by the 1880s it had a large stock of varieties, including many dwarf types. By 1895, 57 types of fruit tree were for sale. These included 28 varieties of apple, 30 plum, 24 peach, six pear, six nectarine, two apricot and three fig.

The Durban Botanic Garden under Keit also provided the public with large quantities of trees. In particular, Keit distributed thousands of *Eucalyptus globulus* (blue gum). Both Keit and Wood were concerned with the deforestation of Natal. Keit felt that silver oak should be planted extensively for use as a firewood. "Firewood', he commented, "even on the coast becomes every year more scarce and valuable". Wood was critical both of blacks for destroying indigenous bush and of settlers for not pursuing tree planing with more vigour. As mentioned previously he also campaigned for the planting of trees in Durban's streets which, though discussed since 1855, had never been systematically undertaken.

Conscious of the fact that Natal imported thousands of pounds worth of timber annually, Wood discussed with Kew the planting of new species of pine in Natal which could compete with foreign imports. Nothing was to come of this, though Wood steadily built up an extensive collection of trees. It is interesting to note that in 1903 T. R. Sim declared that the Durban Botanic Garden contained "most of the trees ever likely to be of commercial value as an object-lesson to anyone who would take up tree-planting".

As far as the raising of fruit trees was concerned Durban was far behind Pietermaritzburg, although it made an abortive attempt to introduce vine cultivation in the early 1870s. At this time Durban garden also imported 376 varieties of fruit trees but, feeling that the climate at the coast was unsuitable for their rearing, the Horticultural Society forwarded them to Sir Theophilus Shepstone for distribution in the Natal Midlands.

The policy of distributing either plants or trees of commercial value benefited not only the shaky Natal economy but also the botanic gardens themselves. The money raised from the increasing sales of plants became essential for the two gardens' own economic survival. This policy of accruing a proportion of revenue from sales had been necessitated by the inadequacy of the Natal Government's grant. As the *Natal Mercury* observed, the botanic gardens had little alternative but to sell plants. However, in spite of Wood's declarations to the contrary, this did mean that both botanic gardens were in open competition with local commercial nurseries.

Nurserymen, led by Leon Ducasse, were outraged that such competition could be allowed in "a civilised, Christian, English colony". They claimed that the two gardens were unfairly subsidized and carried on a "piratical trade" because they received grants, had free rent, rates, and water and had forced down the price of trees by at least 30%. The example was given of eucalyptus seedlings which were costing 15 shillings per 100 in commercial nurseries but only two shillings at the Pietermaritzburg Botanic Garden. This garden's "nefarious trade" with the Boer Republics was greatly resented as it was feared that in the near future the Republics would be able to supply their own markets entirely, especially with fruit.

So effective was Ducasse in his denunciation of "a society trading under the mantle of science" that a special Government Commission met in May 1898 to examine complaints from nurserymen. Though the two botanic gardens were fully exonerated and praised as "a great utility . . . to the colony at large", much harm had been done to their good name. The Pietermaritzburg garden tried to rectify matters by ceasing to distribute free plants and trees, but in vain.

The 1898 Commission was not the first Government investigation into the two gardens. In 1884 a report on botanical enterprise in Natal had criticized the two existing botanic gardens for not contributing enough to colonial development. The Natal Government's concern about the contribution of the two gardens to the Colony mounted during the late 1880s despite the pioneering work of Wood in the herbarium. Finally, in 1890, the Government decided to appoint a Botanic Gardens Commission to investigate botanical enterprise in Natal. This commission was chaired by Sir Theophilus Shepstone and included Messrs Akerman, Bowker, Greenacre and Hime. Shepstone had no illusions about what Natal required:

> "The great want of the country is the discovery and introduction of such products of the soil as can be raised by even small farmers on the different terraces of the colony with a fair prospect of profit, and with the certainty of a market."

To achieve this, Shepstone considered it unnecessary to interfere with the existing functions and uses of the Durban and Pietermaritzburg gardens but rather to establish experimental gardens alongside the existing gardens. He also felt that a third garden should be established, possibly in Newcastle or Charlestown, to serve the upland districts of the Colony. This would create a chain of experimental gardens in the Colony, controlled by one person, based in Durban and under the Department of Forestry. Such re-organisation would entail a large initial expenditure on the part of the Colony, but would yield excellent returns in the long run. Shepstone was at pains to dispel fears of excessive Government interference in the venture. With Wood and Colonel Bowker, he visited the upper districts in search of a suitable site for the third botanic station.

But the unexpected death of Shepstone and the limited powers of the Governor resulted in the dropping of the whole scheme. The Commission report was never published. The Natal Parliament was simply not prepared to spend money on botanical research. As late as 10 December 1898 the *Natal Mercury* was calling for the re-appointment of the botanic commission, but to no avail. It was a short-sighted decision for within a few years it became necessary to establish institutions such as the central experimental farm at Hilton Road.

By 1900 the heyday of botanic gardens in colonial South Africa had passed. A few years earlier T. R. Sim, lamenting the decision to hand control of the King William's Town Botanic Garden over to the local Corporation, had written the following to Kew:

> "The Gardens will become like those of Port Elizabeth and Cape Town, a town garden pure and simple without pretence of having a botanical or experimental connexion . . . what we are in want of most is one really good botanical and experimental garden for the colony, equipped so that it shall not have to earn any part of its own maintenance, and then allow each town to have its own town garden, public park or whatever the local circumstances demand."

For half a century curators had striven to serve the botanical interests of their various regions. That they did not achieve more was due primarily to Government impecunity and to the lack-lustre support of the public. Considering these circumstances it is surprising that any botanic garden survived beyond the initial burst of zeal on the part of its founders. The explanation for this lies in the calibre of such men as MacOwan, Sim and Wood, who in their enthusiasm for the study of botany and for their respective botanic gardens paved the way to Kirstenbosch.

SECTION C: KIRSTENBOSCH

11   The founding of Kirstenbosch

The scholar of botanical history might well be excused for finding himself confused over the state of botanical enterprise in the Western Cape in the troublesome decades straddling the old and the new centuries. While that era sees such notables as Harry Bolus, Peter MacOwan, H. W. R. Marloth and H. H. W. Pearson achieving much, the general flux which affected botanical study is reflected in the vacillating fortunes of botanical institutions and posts. Take, for example, the Chair of Botany at the South African College in Cape Town. In 1858 the enlightened decision had been taken by the Cape authorities to create an official Colonial Botanist, a move long called for by Sir William Hooker, the Director of Kew. Dr Pappe was duly chosen for the position. The following year the college created the Chair of Botany which was filled by the Colonial Botanist, who received £400 per annum. This dual system was not dissimilar to the later arrangement by which the Director of Kirstenbosch was also an honorary Professor of Botany at the University of Cape Town. Following Pappe's death in 1862, the dual appointment passed to Rev. Dr. J. C. Brown who retained it until 1864; the post of Colonial Botanist was eventually abolished in 1866 after Brown returned to his native Scotland.

The Chair of Botany remained in abeyance for 16 years, to be filled only when Peter MacOwan moved from Somerset East to Cape Town in 1880, as mentioned in a previous chapter. Between 1881 and 1889 the post of Curator of the Cape Town Botanic Garden, Curator of the Cape Government Herbarium and Professor of Botany at the South African College were all held by this one man. But in 1889 MacOwan resigned his chair and continued as Curator of the garden only until its downgrading in 1892. In that year he accepted the post of Government Botanist in the Department of Lands, Mines and Agriculture. He remained Curator of the herbarium until shortly before his retirement in 1905. The herbarium was then transferred to the South African Museum. With MacOwan's resignation in 1889, the Chair of Botany lapsed, this time for some 14 years, to be revived thanks to the generosity of Harry Bolus in 1903, when H. H. W. Pearson was imported from the Kew Herbarium to fill the position. This would have been an opportune time to re-establish a botanic garden in or near Cape Town but the Anglo-Boer War (1899–1902) and its aftermath of economic depression and political uncertainty impeded any such development for a number of years.

In 1857 an anonymous writer in the *Cape Monthly Magazine* stated that the city's botanic garden should be at least 200 ha. (500 acres). The idea of establishing a new botanic garden in the vicinity of, but not in, Cape Town was canvassed in 1880, long before the demise of the old garden. In May of that year, the Assistant Director of Kew, W. T. Thiselton-Dyer, addressing the Colonial Institute in London, noted:

> "There certainly seems to be something like a case for the removal of the Cape Botanic Garden into the country along the line of railway, and its reconstruction on a wider and more liberal basis . . . If it were removed out of Cape Town and more liberally organised, it would soon compare favourably with other gardens in the southern hemisphere."

This suggestion was repeated a decade later by J. S. Gamble of the British Indian Forestry Department, who stated that at least 80 ha. (200 acres) should be laid aside for such a purpose at somewhere like Rosebank or Rondebosch.

Kew officials, who carried on a regular exchange of correspondence and plants and seeds with Cape and Natal botanists, were shocked that the former did not possess "a fully equipped botanical institution". It is not surprising that a decline in the contact between Kew and the Cape occurred in the new century since without an established botanic garden with herbarium this was inevitable. Though Kew staff had never neglected to maintain strong links with eminent colonial botanists such as Bolus, as the network of imperial botanic gardens and botanical stations expanded across the globe it was inevitable that links with overseas regions should be increasingly funnelled through such institutions.

For 21 years Cape Town had no botanic garden. That the National Botanic Gardens was finally established at Kirstenbosch was due to two factors. The first was the creation of the dominion of the Union of South Africa on 31 May 1910. This unification opened the way for the formation of a botanical institution which could serve the whole of the subcontinent. The second factor was the initiative taken in 1910 by Professor Pearson. Henry Harold Welch Pearson was the first of a number of botanists closely connected with Kirstenbosch who also had firm ties with Kew and with Cambridge University.

Pearson was a product of both institutions, had had colonial botanical experience in Ceylon and, at the time of his appointment as the first Bolus Professor of Botany at Cape Town in 1903, was assistant for India in the Kew Herbarium. This 33-year-old Professor was to excel as a lecturer and as a researcher. He also collected botanical specimens on the western side of southern Africa as far north as Angola. Many contemporary observers noted Pearson's charm but he was also a very strong-willed and determined man, qualities he had needed to survive under the dictatorial rule of the then Director of Kew, Sir William Thiselton-Dyer.

On 10 November 1910, less than six months after the creation of a united South Africa, Pearson made his address as President of Section C of the South African Association for the Advancement of Science. He proposed that a Government department of botany be established, centred on a new botanic garden with its own herbarium, libary, museum and laboratories. This garden should be in the Cape Peninsula. Pearson was particularly keen that the National Botanic Gardens should specialize in preserving and studying the indigenous flora of South Africa. He proposed that the garden should be financed along the lines of the Peradeniya garden in Ceylon, that is, receive a fixed proportion of the State's revenue. In South Africa's case this would have amounted to an unrealistic sum in excess of £30 000 a year. In this respect, Pearson perhaps overplayed his hand. With the national economy far from healthy, General Botha's new Government was not going to consider such expenditure. It was to be over two and a half years before Parliament approved a resolution in favour of establishing a national botanic garden. In that period the means of governing and financing the new institution were worked out. The exact site of the garden was also chosen.

The selection of the site

As far as Pearson and his associates were concerned, the new national botanic garden had to be in the Western Cape on the Cape Peninsula. Their reasoning was that the Western Cape was rich in flora and was near the sea, that the climate was suitable for the growing of a large number of South African plants, that the Bolus Herbarium was there, that the region was associated with the pioneers of South African botany and, lastly, that a suitable site was available for a garden. To these points must be added the fact that the scheme was very much initiated and controlled by Capetonians.

Few would question the location of the mother garden in the Cape, though by virtue of past performance Durban had first claim to the new institution. Such a suggestion was summarily dismissed because of Durban's subtropical climate. Interestingly, it was to be a later criticism of the Kirstenbosch site that it had too damp a climate. Criticism may be levelled that Durban with its established grounds and fine herbarium was not chosen as the first satellite garden in the National Botanic Gardens network. Equally unfortunate was the fact that the Rand area was not accommodated in some manner since the unification of South Africa had firmly established the centre of power in Pretoria; but in the early years of its existence the National Botanic Gardens was very much a Cape phenomenon. As will be seen, this had the disastrous consequence of dividing South African botany into north and south, which culminated in the establishment of the separate institution of the Pretoria National Botanic Garden.

N. S. Pillans (1884–1964) not only suggested the Kirstenbosch site to Pearson but for many decades after its founding supported the National Botanic Gardens.

In 1911 little thought was given to such possible future problems; the main concern was to find a suitable site for the new garden on the Cape Peninsula. It was clear that the site must be on crown land as there was no money available to purchase land. The "historic ground" of the Groote Schuur estate on the eastern slopes of Table Mountain was the obvious choice as there was a considerable stretch of available land where a site could be selected. The story of Pearson, G. H. Ridley, the Curator of what was now called the Cape Town Municipal Botanic Garden, and the young enthusiastic Rosebank botanist, Neville S. Pillans, setting off in a Cape cart one February morning in 1911 to find a site for the garden is well known. Pearson apparently wanted it to be in the region of the Rondebosch woods, near to where the present University of Cape Town is situated, but Pillans favoured a spot further down the Peninsula. When they eventually arrived at Pillans' site, Pearson was so struck by the majesty of the landscape that he simply said, "This is the place." They were standing under the shadow of Castle Rock on the site of the derelict farm Kirstenbosch.

One wing of the old Kirstenbosch homestead about 1900.

The Kirstenbosch estate

The farm of Kirstenbosch is historically interesting in its own right. Its status changed on no fewer than seven occasions before it passed in trust to the governing body of the National Botanic Gardens. Several theories have been suggested concerning the origin of the name but it seems too much of a coincidence that it was not named after a member of the Kirsten family who lived in the vicinity in the eighteenth century, though no definite link between the family and the farm has been established. Originally the area was called Leendertsbos after Leenderts Cornelissen of Zevenhuysen, a *vrijtimmerman* or free sawyer. This occupation arose because Van Riebeeck was conscious of the need to provide Cape Town with a steady and reliable supply of timber. This could be done only with responsible forest management, therefore rather than throw the forests on the south-east of the Peninsula open to all, he allocated the forest on the very frontier of the settlement to Cornelissen in October 1657. The property itself was not alienated from the Company.

Cornelissen worked the forest with free servants and with slaves. Van Riebeeck recorded in his journal on 25 October 1658:

> "Today another slave belonging to the sawyer Leendert Cornelissen deserted, notwithstanding the fact that he treats his slaves the best of all the freemen."

Seven months later the journal noted:

> "Leendert Cornelissen of Zevenhuysen had been

attacked in his forest by 50 to 60 Hottentots yesterday about an hour before dusk. He received only a slight assegai wound in the neck, since his men, armed with guns, had come upon the scene just in time and had put the Hottentots to flight immediately."

The raiding of these Khoi Khoi from the Hout Bay region eventually prompted Van Riebeeck in February 1660 to order the planting of the famous hedge of indigenous bitter almond *(Brabejum stellatifolium)* and the building of wooden observation towers along the eastern boundary of the settlement. Remains of this "hedge" survive in Kirstenbosch to this day and since 1936 the hedge has been a National Monument.

By the time the barrier had established itself, Leendertsbos had reverted to direct Company control. In May 1660 Cornelissen had been elected a burgher Councillor but his tendency to rough and debauched behaviour, drinking, fighting and swearing, resulted in his dismissal from the Council in October 1661. What became of him is not known, but in the 1670s Leendertsbos was part of a Company post.

Although some three to four hours from Cape Town and under the protection of a Superintendent who lived at Kirstenbosch, much of the best timber had been extracted from the area by the time the British took final possession of the Cape in 1806. The continuity of official ownership continued for only another five years. In 1811, the year the property was divided and sold, the traveller and botanist William Burchell visited Kirstenbosch and was awestruck by its natural beauty. He wrote of the spot:

> "The view from this spot ['hill of Wynberg'] and indeed all the scenery around, is the most picturesque of any I had seen in the vicinity of Cape Town. The beauties here displayed to the eye could scarcely be represented by the most skilful pencil . . . The objects immediately surrounding us were purely sylvan . . . Here I beheld [Nature's] perfection in the sweet harmony of soft colours and tints of every gradation, speaking a language which all may understand, transfusing into the soul a delight which all may enjoy, and which never fails, at least for the time, to smother every uneasy sensation of the mind."

Burchell was especially impressed by the many large silver trees *(Leucadendron argenteum)* in the area. Plant species he had not encountered before included: *Anthericum graminifolium, Moroea gladiata, Penaea acuta* and *Protea grandiflora.*

The purchasers of the divided Kirstenbosch, each taking about 92 ha. (227 acres), were the Colonial Secretary, Henry Alexander, and the Deputy Colonial Secretary, Colonel Christopher Bird. Bird's section consisted of the upper part of the estate and included the old Company house, the ruins of which lie today at the top of the Cape chestnut avenue. Though Bird soon sold his section to Alexander for £1 000, he left one interesting landmark. He constructed a small pool, appropriately shaped like a bird. The pool was fed by a spring and lined with bricks which may have been ship's ballast bricks from Java or possibly have come from the less distant Bottelary hills. The pool has often incorrectly been referred to as Lady Anne's Bath. In later years Bird became the whipping boy of some of the 1820 settlers from Ireland who were sent to Clanwilliam, and he was the subject of a biting political pamphlet entitled *Jesuits Unmasked.*

Alexander lived at Kirstenbosch in a house he built on the site of the present tea room. Though the area had long since ceased to be a frontier farm it was still fairly wild. Indigenous forest existed on the upper slopes of the mountain and "wolves" (jackals?) were present on the estate. After Alexander's death Kirstenbosch once more reverted to the Government but was once again divided and sold in 1823. Forty hectares were joined to a neighbouring estate and the bulk of the estate passed to the Eksteen family and hence in 1853, through marriage, to the Cloetes. For 72 years these two families farmed the Kirstenbosch estate. They laid out vegetable gardens, orchards and vineyards. Sadly no comment on Kirstenbosch wine has survived. This period also sees the planting of a large number of oaks *(Quercus robur)* which provided acorns for the famous black pigs of Kirstenbosch. Inevitably the management of the estate as a working farm resulted in the destruction of much indigenous vegetation, including a large number of silver trees and substantial sections of the bitter almond hedge.

FIRST ANNUAL REPORT

OF

The South African Immigration Association,

CAPE TOWN.

1901. — 1902.

SOUTH AFRICAN IMMIGRATION ASSOCIATION.

Before proceeding to report on the work done by the S.A.I.A. since its inauguration in 1901, it seems fitting that its origin should be traced, and a tribute paid to the man to whom the Association owes so much.

By a fortunate accident, the late Mr. Rhodes had noticed in passing up his avenue to Groote Schuur, at Rondebosch a number of women who went to Mrs. Bairnsfather for advice, and asked her how she accounted for their presence. And so it came about that he heard from her of the work that was going on in connection with immigration and of the great difficulty and hindrance to its success owing to the absence of a home for new arrivals in Cape Town, where the immigrants could stay while awaiting employment, or until put in touch with suitable work. Later on in 1900 Mr. Rhodes told Mrs. Bairnsfather that he would help her when the right time came, and he was true to his word as the following letter proves :—

Groote Schuur.

DEAR MRS. BAIRNSFATHER,

I have an old house without roof at Kirstenbosch if you can get a reasonable estimate for repairs I will do it but do not ask me for too much as my obligations are heavy. I will then hire it to your Society for 21 years at 5/- a year.

Yours. C. J. RHODES.

Letter from Rhodes about the old Kirstenbosch homestead.

Kirstenbosch in about 1890, 23 years before the establishment of the National Botanic Gardens on this site. The cottage was the first house of the curator. Above the cottage is a vineyard where today rockeries, aloes and annuals decorate the area. The hedge in the foreground was removed when the present avenues of ficus and camphor trees were planted by Cecil John Rhodes.

Cecil John Rhodes, owner of the Kirstenbosch estate, 1895–1902.

In 1866 the small Church of the Good Shepherd was built by Bishop Gray just outside the estate boundary. It was rebuilt in 1880 and extended in 1904. For some time now a special service has been held annually in the church on "Kirstenbosch Sunday" which is attended by many of those connected with the garden.

In 1895 Cecil Rhodes bought the Kirstenbosch estate, then consisting of 130 ha. (320 acres) for £9 000. This purchase was part of his scheme to buy as much property as possible on the east side of Table Mountain and preserve it from urban development. Though he planted the avenues of camphor, Moreton Bay figs and Spanish chestnuts, by the turn of the century the estate was much neglected. One significant development for later generations was the road he laid out across the lower park of the estate almost to Constantia Nek. This was densely lined with trees but was not opened to the public until 1923. About the same time as the road was built, a state Forestry nursery for exotic plantation trees was established above the estate.

In Rhodes' will Kirstenbosch was left to the State as part of the Groote Schuur estate. In the Edwardian period it lay derelict, the vineyards and orchards overgrown and the old farm house, which had been empty since the mid-1890s, a ruin. The area was, however, noted for its wild flowers and was a popular picnic spot for Capetonians.

"A mere bagatelle": the establishment of Kirstenbosch

Following his 1910 speech, Pearson soon realized that his ideas concerning the financing and control of the future National Botanic Gardens would have to be modified. When it became clear that the Government did not want direct control over the garden, Pearson pressed for it being closely linked with the South African College. He went as far as suggesting that the college's laboratories, greenhouses, botanical library and newly acquired herbarium all be re-allocated to the new garden.

The selection of the Kirstenbosch site in 1911 did not hasten the establishment of the garden. Pearson canvassed support from Kew and from botanists and public figures in South Africa. A Committee of 14 was set up to promote the campaign for the establishment of the garden. It included Lord de Villiers and the eminent amateur botanist, Rudolph Marloth, then Professor of Chemistry at Stellenbosch University. Support also came from the mining magnate and politician, Sir Lionel Phillips. He and Lady Phillips did much to promote the concept of the garden in influential political circles. Indeed it was Phillips who eventually proposed in Parliament in May 1913 the resolution to establish a national botanic garden.

Sir Lionel Phillips' speech in the House of Assembly lasted for nearly an hour. He specifically advocated the Kirstenbosch site, claiming it to be nearer to Cape Town than Kew was to London or the botanic gardens at Lisbon and Berlin were to those cities. He urged that the garden should be linked to the South African College and not the Department of Agriculture and he demanded that as well as a director and a curator, the garden should have two gardeners and 10 labourers.

Phillips made two controversial points in his speech. His attack on the Forestry Department for planting exotic trees on the slopes of Table Mountain may have been understandable but it would have been better left unsaid; Kirstenbosch in its infant years needed all the friends it could find. Phillips also stressed the need for concentrating on the study of indigenous plants. He sat down amid loud cheers. Sir Percy FitzPatrick and John X. Merriman followed him, giving speeches in favour of the scheme. Merriman stated that it would cost "a mere bagetelle" to establish the National Botanic Gardens and much benefit would come from it. In particular he hoped its establishment would lead to the founding of "a school in gardening".

On behalf of the Government, the Prime Minister, General Louis Botha, said that he was sympathetic to the founding of the garden. He was, however, non-committal about Government support for the project and even about the location of the institution.

The resolution to establish the National Botanic Gardens was passed unanimously by the House of Assembly. There followed negotiations between Phillips and Botha. The Prime Minister, who was also Minister of Agriculture, was anxious that the new garden would not duplicate the work done by that ministry. He was emphatic that the garden should be partly self-financing and that, while the Government would give an annual grant of £1 000 and an initial sum of £2 500 to facilitate the building of a director's house and a small laboratory, the garden should not be a Government institution. The site of Kirstenbosch was also officially agreed upon; the land would remain Government property but would be under the control of a Board of Trustees for as long as the botanic garden survived.

This Board of Trustees would contain five members, three of whom would be Government appointees, the fourth a nominee of the Cape Town Municipality and the fifth a representative of a National Botanic Society, which it was proposed should be established. This Society was duly formed on 10 June 1913 with the aims of supporting Kirstenbosch by supplementing the Government grant with subscriptions; of creating a link between the garden and the general public; and of generally fostering interest in and expanding knowledge about South African flora.

The original board consisted of Lord de Villiers, Sir Lionel Phillips and Sir David de Villiers Graaff as the Government appointees; the Mayor representing the Municipality; and W. Duncan Baxter, who was to have long association with Kirstenbosch, as the nominee of the Botanical Society. When Lord de Villiers died in 1914, his place was taken by Sir Ernest Kilpin.

On 16 June 1913 the Board met for the first time and appointed Pearson as honorary Director: he retained his Chair of Botany, which provided his income. A Curator, in charge of horticulture and the general running of the garden, a gardener, a ranger and a secretary were also appointed. On 1 July the Government handed over about 133 ha. (330 acres) of the Kirstenbosch estate to the care of the Board of Trustees. The legal transfer was not effected until February 1915. Before that, in December 1913, the Government had also allowed the garden an additional 61 ha. (150 acres) from the adjacent Klaassenbosch estate.

H. H. W. Pearson (1870–1916), the first director of the National Botanic Gardens (1913–16).

Professor and Mrs Pearson lived at first in the rather primitive conditions of the stables of the old Alexander farmhouse. In 1915 they moved to the director's new house, situated on a ridge overlooking the centre of the garden, in an area where silver trees grew and where substantial numbers of new trees of this species were subsequently planted. It was appropriate that his new home was surrounded with the trees Burchell had been so enamoured of at Kirstenbosch a hundred years earlier, for Pearson was first and foremost an enthusiast of indigenous flora. Duncan Baxter later claimed that Pearson's main interest was the Cape's flora. This is not altogether fair criticism, but the geographical location of Kirstenbosch naturally favoured work on the flora of the Western Cape.

Many years before the National Botanic Gardens was founded Harry Bolus referred to the "gloomy impression that the south-west [Cape] flora is dying out and is doomed to extinction". This was a belief which became the subject of much debate in the opening decade of the twentieth century. In his famous 1910 speech Pearson firmly stated:

"The South African Botanic Garden cannot be merely an economic undertaking; it must also be an expression of the intellectual and artistic aspirations of the New Nation whose duty it is to foster the study of the country which it occupies, to encourage a proper appreciation of the rare and beautiful with which Nature has so lovingly endowed it."

Of the collecting of South African flora and its dispatch to Europe for study there he was equally outspoken: "This is surely not in harmony with the traditions of South African patriotism". Another advocate of this botanical nationalism was Neville Pillans, who had complained in the *Agricultural Journal* that no public garden in the country could be considered "exclusively South African in type". It was such an indigenous garden that Pearson wished to establish at Kirstenbosch.

Pearson had as his Curator Joseph William Mathews, a Kew-trained man from Cheshire who had worked in the Cape Town Public Gardens Department and had later run a local nursery. Kirstenbosch has been fortunate in having Curators whose high calibre has complimented the national standing of its four directors. The curator has on more than one occasion been able to provide continuity between one director and his successor. Mathews was Curator from 1913 to 1936; Frank Thorns and H. F. Werner followed, both Kew men and both serving 11 years each as Curator. From 1959 to 1979 the post was held by Mr Jack Marais who was succeeded by John Winter who had also received his training at Kew. It is worth recording that prior to 1953 "Kewites" who worked as gardeners at Kirstenbosch included F. J. Cook, L. B. Creasey, H. F. Davies, G. A. Davis, Harry Hall, H. M. Holloway and A. W. Maynard.

In 1913 Pearson and Mathews set about planning the garden with much energy. First of all they established the now famous fern dell. The old "bird" pool was cleaned out, the bed of the stream was paved and a small cave and a waterfall were built, around which were planted ferns and streptocarpus. At the bottom of this small valley a 200-square-metre nursery was established and in the natural amphitheatre above the bath Pearson planted over 400 cycads. In his annual report for 1915 he stated:

"This collection is one of which any of the great botanic gardens of the world might well be proud and it offers unique opportunities for the study of a group of very exceptional scientific interest."

Four kilometres of paths were laid out, as was an avenue of Cape chestnuts which ran up to the ruins of the old Company house. Fourteen seats were placed near these pathways. An "aloe koppie" was established but this later failed, as did the Bolus orchid garden. More successful were the beds prepared near the entrance which contained many succulents. The building of a terrace in the garden was also begun.

Of momentous importance was the decision to establish a great lawn of indigenous grasses in a swampy area around the lower part of the stream which flowed out of the bath. This lawn was later expanded. It provided a place for visitors to picnic and was relatively easy to maintain. It also afforded a degree of safety to both people and to the surrounding plants. The decision to open up this area in the middle of the garden profoundly affected its character: Kirstenbosch has the air of an open, as distinct from an intimate, garden which is dominated by the majestic backdrop of Table Mountain.

Pearson continued in a small way the growing of economics, and in 1915 began taking meteorological readings in the garden: a traditional function of botanic gardens in the British empire. Though Pearson allocated areas for particular genera such as *Pelargonium* and the Compositae family, no serious attempt was made at first to group plants on a systematic basis. Whether this was Pearson's intention is not altogether clear. His successor, Professor Compton, later asserted, "The idea of 'landscaping' Kirstenbosch was always rendered futile by the grandeur and diversity of its setting". Compton's successor, Professor Rycroft, defended the informality of Kirstenbosch on the basis that a systematic arrangement was ecologically unsuitable and aesthetically unsatisfactory. Pearson, however, did obviously feel that he needed some guidance in laying out the garden as he appealed to Kew for help. It was agreed that Kew's assistant director, William J. Bean, author of *The Royal Botanic Gardens, Kew: historical and descriptive*, should sail to Cape Town to offer Pearson some expert advice.

Two disasters then befell Kirstenbosch. In 1914 the World War I broke out, preventing Bean's visit and resulting in a 25% cut in the Government grant. Twenty-four years later the then Director of Kew, Sir Arthur Hill, wrote to Kirstenbosch of Bean's having to abort his trip, "This was most unfortunate, for not only would valuable advice have resulted, but the ties between the two institutions would thus have been further strengthened". The second disaster was equally serious. On 3 November 1916 Professor Pearson died, aged 46. He was buried on the southern slopes of the dell at Kirstenbosch under a Celtic cross: his epitaph is that of Wren, "If ye seek his monument, look around". Nearby stands an Atlas cedar presented by Kew in 1916.

In the interim before a new director took up his position in March 1919, the garden struggled to survive. The Curator, Frank Cartwright, and Duncan Baxter tried their best to maintain what had been achieved and to develop the garden wherever practical. Four hundred protea bushes were planted, the lily pond was dug and the building of the terrace system continued. Finance remained the major problem. Income was derived from the Government and Cape Town Corporation grants, contributions from the Botanical Society and the sale of plants, seeds, wood, acorns, soil and gravel. Total income did not exceed £3 000 until 1919. In the years 1914 to 1920, a third of Kirstenbosch's revenue was derived from the sale to the general public of wood and acorns. Little had changed since Peter MacOwan had commented that South African botany had to carry on a "perpetual fight against insolvency".

Pearson had hoped that the sale of useful economics would greatly assist the garden's income. By 1917 belladonna, buchu, carobs, castor beans, bush tea, *Madia sativa*, melons, olives, rosemary, soya beans, sugar beans and sweet potatoes were being experimented with at Kirstenbosch. But these were not, as Pearson had predicted, to be of "far-reaching importance to a pastoral and agricultural South Africa". In 1917 an official report condemned the National Botanic Gardens for its policy on economics, stating the experiments should be taken over by the Government. The report also questioned the wisdom of maintaining the link with the South African College as this inevitably made the garden a purely local institution.

It was this situation of near-bankruptcy, official censure and a limited number of visitors—there was only one bus a week to the garden from Cape Town—which later prompted General Smuts to say, "This place was born in criticism". That Kirstenbosch was not reduced to a public park like the Cape's nineteenth-century botanic garden was in no small part due to the tenacity of Pearson's successors. Robert Harold Compton was made Director at the age of 33 in 1919 and remained in this position for 34

R. H. Compton (1886–1979), Pearson's successor as director (1919–53).

The seedroom and greenhouses in the Kirstenbosch nursery about 1920.

years until 1953. Hedley Brian Rycroft was in his mid-thirties when he succeeded Professor Compton and he served 29 years as Director before his retirement in 1983, when the present Director, Professor Jacobus N. Eloff, was appointed as his successor.

Although only 13 years separated Pearson and Compton, they were men from different eras: Pearson was a Victorian; Compton, in his tweeds, was an English gentleman of the early twentieth century. The latter had a great respect for the former. When walking through the garden in the mid-1920s with the eminent forester H. G. Fourcade, Compton remembered that it was the anniversary of Pearson's death. The two men made their way to the grave and placed a cycad leaf on it as a mark of respect. Pearson's name was suitably commemorated when the University of Cape Town created a new Chair of Botany especially for the director of the National Botanic Gardens and named it the Harold Pearson Chair of Botany; 75% of the salary for this post was paid by the Government. The existing Chair was named the Harry Bolus Chair of Botany, the first appointment under this title being that of the Cambridge graduate, David Thoday in 1918. The director was now relieved of much of the teaching and administrative load connected with the university which Pearson had had to carry. It also meant that all the garden's administration could be moved from Cape Town to Kirstenbosch.

The garden's annual report for Compton's first full year made sad reading:

> "The inadequacy of income was responsible for deplorable results. Not only was development almost unthinkable but the degeneration of roads and paths, nursery stock, labels and so on was only too evident: and much of the loss occasioned is almost irreparable. At one time the curator had no skilled gardener in his charge and the labourers' wages were reduced to a total of £16 a week."

Worst of all, large numbers of plants were dying. A Commission reported the following year on the National Botanic Gardens. It was generally sympathetic to the plight of the garden but its detailed recommendations came to nothing as the Government was not prepared to increase its annual grant dramatically. For Compton and Rycroft money remained the perennial problem. The Government grant had to be supplemented by grants from the Botanical Society; the Cape Town Municipality, whose grant did not reach £1 500 until 1955, the level of the Government grant in 1920; the Provincial and Divisional Councils; and after 1944, from the South African Railways: the S.A.R. had for many years before this transported specimens free of charge for Kirstenbosch. In later years on certain days of the week a small entrance fee has been levied on those who are not members of the Botanical Society. Depending on the source of the director's salary after 1941 a sum of £400 or £500 was reimbursed by either the University of Cape Town or Kirstenbosch to the other institution.

The Government grant itself increased slowly during the 1920s and 30s and by 1940 it was £4 000. Only in the 1950s did it increase significantly: in 1952, for example, it stood at £16 000. By 1984 it formed nearly 90% of the garden's total income, a rise of 47% from 1915 and an indication of a fact that should have been realised many years before: botanic gardens cannot fulfil their proper functions unless predominantly State financed.

A source of income which, while averaging only £600 a year between 1913 and 1960, greatly assisted Compton in the early years of his directorship was the sale of plants and in particular the sale of buchu, a species of the Rutaceae family. By infusing the leaves of this indigenous plant in vinegar brandy or "dop", buchu vinegar or brandy could be made, which was used in the Cape for sundry internal medical complaints. MacOwan had been somewhat sceptical about its medicinal properties, claiming that, "its chief value perhaps is the excuse and cover it affords for the occasional dose of alcohol".

Between 1924 and 1931 Kirstenbosch received a small Government grant to experiment with economics, this despite earlier Government hostility in 1917 to such practices. Compton experimented with a wide range of species, including fodder crops, root crops, grasses, teas and edible seeds. In 1924 he managed to acquire a 55-litre still. In 1922 and 1933 lists of medicinal and aromatic plants of economic value in cultivation at Kirstenbosch were published by the *Journal of the Botanical Society*. However, by the latter date most of the work in this field had been suspended: a lack of money and specialized staff, a slow response from farmers and opposition from the Ministry of Agriculture being the reasons.

Although 45% of seeds offered for sale from Kirstenbosch in 1921 were from exotic species, Compton firmly believed that Pearson's policy of creating an indigenous garden was correct and it was Compton who established Kirstenbosch's reputation internationally as the prototype of the national indigenous garden. The acquisition of an extra 275 ha. (680 acres) above the garden on the slopes of Table Mountain, now called the upper Kirstenbosch nature reserve, was a considerable boon to this scheme. The area contained natural ravine forest; it held much of the catchment area of the Liesbeek River; and because it rose to Maclear's Beacon (1 240m) on the summit of the mountain, the National Botanic Gardens had now, in a relatively small area, an altitude range of over 1 000 metres.

In the 1920s and 1930s Compton, assisted by Mathews and later Thorns, laid out the garden giving it the general character it has today. An infrastructure of water and drainage systems was installed, based on a small quarter-million-litre reservoir which was also constructed. The tea room and a braai area were added to the amenities and the famous sundial was placed in its setting. In the mid

The early economic garden at Kirstenbosch.

The staff of the National Botanic Gardens at Kirstenbosch, 1936.

to late 1930s an entrance complex of gates, bell tower and assistant curator's cottage was built at a new entrance site. The tower was a gift from Lady Phillips to commemorate her husband. Plant concentrations included mesembryanthemums, pelargoniums, cycads, proteas and ericas. A succulent rock garden, later named after Mathews, was built, a new nursery was constructed and in 1939 a large succulent conservatory was erected.

Both Mathews and Thorns fought what seemed an endless battle against moles, which were especially destructive in the bulb nursery. In 1935 a mole-proof concrete barrier 1,5 metres deep and standing only 23 cm. above ground level was erected around this nursery. Even so it was to be another two years before moles were finally banished from sampling the delights of ixia, freesia, babiana, gladiolus, watsonia and massonia bulbs.

Despite the problems of finding a reliable labour force and of accommodating it, and of attracting visitors when there was no regular bus service from Cape Town (this began only in 1938), by the late 1920s Kirstenbosch was receiving over 60 000 visitors annually. In 1927 Sir George Taylor, a future director of Kew, visited Kirstenbosch. Years later he wrote:

> "With its superlative backcloth of mountain buttresses, for sheer grandeur the setting of Kirstenbosch is unsurpassed . . . The only other botanic garden which in my estimation approaches the grandeur of Kirstenbosch is that of Rio de Janeiro."

When Kirstenbosch celebrated its Silver Jubilee in 1938, Pearson's ideal of an indigenous garden was well on its way to being achieved. The enthusiasm for such a garden was certainly to be found, and in the closing years of the decade a campaign against exotic invaders in the garden and reserve was waged and the old silver tree forest partly replanted. If fault could be found with the direction which Kirstenbosch was taking, it was that it was still too Cape-orientated. Frank Thorns openly spoke of the need to plant more species from Natal and Zululand. The University of Cape Town's decision in the 1930s to withdraw the Bolus Herbarium and Library, which it had placed in the garden in 1924, in one respect proved of long-term benefit for Kirstenbosch since it forced the garden to look out into the whole of South Africa for specimens for the herbarium which it had to start. It is unfortunate that Kirstenbosch still, however, had only one satellite garden, the Karoo Garden established at Whitehill, Matjiesfontein, in 1921, which was transferred to Worcester in 1945. No serious consideration was given to establishing an affiliated garden outside the Cape Province.

The curatorship of Frank Thorns is important because of the diversity of species that were being planted. In particular he increased the garden's collection of aloes until, at the time of his departure to run the Durban Parks Department, it numbered 141 varieties. In later years Harry Hall built on this foundation, creating a superb collection of succulents. Thorns also put in a large number of indigenous trees and laid out beds of such decorative species as kniphofia and watsonia.

The Second World War was not as devastating in its effects on Kirstenbosch as had been the First. Five members of staff went away on service leaving Compton and Thorns with only two assistants. Thorns complained bitterly that this created great problems as their labour was "of the type requiring regular supervision". None the less, and despite the fact that many botanical journals en route from Kew to Kirstenbosch "went down", the garden emerged from the war and immediate post-war years relatively unscathed. Kirstenbosch was even in a position to help Singapore Botanic Gardens re-establish itself after the end of the Japanese occupation.

The post-war years proved crucial for the garden's financial survival. In 1934 the financial load on the institution had been lessened following the publication of a second report on the garden. The Department of Public Works was henceforth responsible for maintaining the garden's roads and buildings. This had not solved the financial problems of Kirstenbosch, however. In 1948 a third report on the garden stated that it must have more money, but it was not until 1953 when Kirstenbosch was

Bird's bath before development.

Professor H. B. Rycroft, director from 1954 to 1983, created the National Botanic Gardens as a truly national institution.

classified a State-aided institution that it began to emerge from perpetual penury. Between 1952 and 1962 the Government grant quadrupled.

Professor Rycroft: Kirstenbosch and the regional gardens

In 1954, after being in existence for 41 years, Kirstenbosch acquired its first South African born Director. This was Hedley Brian Rycroft. Professor Rycroft, a Natalian, was a trained botanist and forester who had a special interest in proteas; indeed he did much to popularize the commercial growing of many species of this genus. Professor Rycroft's scientific work on Proteaceae has in recent years been ably continued by Dr. John Rourke, currently the Curator of the Compton Herbarium at Kirstenbosch.

Professor Rycroft was Director for 30 years; he retired in 1983 and moved to the south coast of Natal to run the Skyline Arboretum and Nature Reserve. He has recently moved to live in Hogsback. In his time as Director of Kirstenbosch he did more than his two illustrious predecessors in establishing a truly national botanical institution. In the garden itself a 54-million-litre (12-million-gallon) dam was constructed on Silver Tree ridge and the road which bisected Kirstenbosch was diverted to the lower boundary, both of which improvements were of fundamental importance to the development of the

garden. Winning a campaign to prevent a freeway cutting through Kirstenbosch was equally significant.

Although in 1962 Kirstenbosch acquired 30 ha. (74 acres) of the adjoining Fernwood estate, making the garden's total area 527 ha. (1 300 acres), the fundamental structure of the garden remained as it had long been established. Professor Rycroft did open up the lower garden somewhat and the famous "garden clock" was donated in 1970 by the Rotary Club of Rondebosch, but the significant developments lay elsewhere.

Professor Rycroft, ably assisted by his Curator, Mr. Jack Marais, and by Mr. Alec Middlemost, advocated not only a policy of preserving and promoting the growing of indigenous flora but also one of campaigning against exotic plants. Though funds were still limited there was more money available to promote indigenous flowers in particular, both in South Africa and abroad. The Rycroft era saw Kirstenbosch-grown flowers exhibited with considerable success overseas. South Africa's indigenous flora also received considerable international publicity from the Kirstenbosch Golden Jubilee celebrations in 1963. This extravaganza lasted for 10 months and included a botanical tour of South Africa by 45 invited foreign botanists from Argentina, Australia, Austria, Belgium, Denmark, Great Britain, Finland, France, Italy, the Netherlands, New Zealand, Norway, Portugal, Sweden, the United States and West Germany, as well as Rhodesia and South West Africa.

The Kirstenbosch garden was by the 1950s so well established that the Director was in a position to turn his attention to developing one of Pearson's proposals: the establishment throughout South Africa of a series of satellite regional gardens affiliated to Kirstenbosch.

The concept of regional gardens was by no means novel, even in Pearson's time. Dr. John Lindley, one of the co-founders of the *Gardeners' Chronicle*, noted in his 1839 official report on the Royal Botanic Gardens, Kew:

> "A national garden ought to be the centre round which all minor establishments of the same nature should be arranged; they should all be under the control of the chief of that garden, acting in concert with him and through him with one another, reporting constantly their proceedings, explaining their wants, receiving their supplies, and aiding the mother country in everything that is useful in the vegetable kingdom."

Forty-one years later the Director of Kew, when discussing the dozen or so institutions in the Cape Colony which claimed to be botanic gardens, suggested: "All these gardens should be affiliated in some degree to the metropolitan establishment at Cape Town". Nothing came of this proposal although it is not improbable that it influenced Pearson in his thinking. The system of interconnected British imperial botanic gardens and botanic stations in the nineteenth century worked with varying degrees of success. The exchange of plants

Bird's bath about 1962 after development.

and seeds between institutions was one of the fundamental elements in colonial development, but the formal linking of botanical institutions tended to work only when controlled by the imperial Government, which in reality meant by Kew. Without a firm overall direction, personal animosity between curators and regional rivalry tended to nullify inter-regional development.

In his 1910 speech Pearson stated that each region in South Africa would need at least one experimental garden, which would mean a minimum of 10 would have to be founded. The administration of such a network would have to be at the Cape Town garden, which would appoint the curator for each regional garden. Periodic visits of senior officials of the National Botanic Gardens would have to be made to these regional gardens and their curators would occasionally have to visit the parent garden.

Three years later the Prime Minister said, "It might be essential to have several botanic gardens, perhaps under a single control". Sir Percy FitzPatrick was more precise and advocated research specifically into Karoo vegetation. Despite the untimely death of Pearson, this idea was upheld by Compton.

In 1921 J. D. Logan gave 16 ha. (40 acres) adjacent to the railway line at Whitehill near Matjiesfontein for a Karoo Botanic Garden. This remote spot in the western Karoo, north of the Witteberg range and some 325 kilometres (200 miles) from Kirstenbosch, had been chosen the previous year by Compton and Pillans. It was an excellent site in which to grow and study succulents as the annual rainfall rarely rose above 125 mm. (five inches). The garden's running costs were financed through voluntary contributions and by the sale of seeds, but in effect it was supported and run by the South African Railways. The Curator was Joseph Archer, the former Station Master at Matjiesfontein. He was helped by the Railways' horticulturalist, Frank Frith, who in 1925 created an award-winning South African succulent garden at the Empire Exhibition in London. The Railways also brought in water-tanker trucks in time of drought and local Railways staff helped the curator when necessary. Visits of Kirstenbosch staff culminated in 1931 in the publication of a flora of the Whitehill district by the Royal Society of South Africa.

Although Whitehill was an interesting garden, few people visited such a remote spot. A combination of drought, a new national road and little public support, especially during the Second World War, forced Kirstenbosch in 1946 to vacate the Whitehill site and re-establish the Karoo Garden in a site donated the year before by the Worcester Municipality, four kilometres (3 miles) north of that town and less than half the distance by road from Kirstenbosch that Whitehill was. Jacques Thudichum, a Swiss horticulturalist and former cattle rancher in Argentina, served as Curator from 1945 to 1958. He was responsible for laying out an attractive garden from a foundation of plants transferred from Whitehill. The garden was formally opened by Governor-General van Zyl in September 1948. Sensibly it was affiliated financially with Kirstenbosch, which in part explains this regional garden's success.

The garden also received an annual grant from the Worcester Municipality. Proximity to Worcester, the energy and pleasant personality of Frank Stayner, the second Curator, and an active local branch of the Botanical Society have also ensured this garden's survival. In 1956 the Karoo Garden was twice increased in size through donations, once from the local Municipality and once from C. H. Heathie. The garden was again expanded in 1980. Today the Karoo Garden covers 119 ha. (294 acres) and is celebrated not only for its fine collection of aloes and other succulents but also for its dramatic floral display of semi-arid species. In 1980 the garden, then under the curatorship of Mr. Bruce Bayer, was recognized by the International Organisation for Succulent Plant Study as one of only six gardens in the world with a collection of succulents of outstanding scientific merit.

Professor Rycroft took over the direction of the re-established Karoo Botanic Garden when it was nearly a decade old. In September 1938 in a radio broadcast Compton had said:

> "Kirstenbosch is a distinctively national South African institution and deserves the support of all who love the beautiful and interesting things which this country possesses in such profusion."

That he did not press ahead with establishing other regional gardens is unfortunate. The sad experience of Whitehill, constant financial problems and a not always happy relationship with botanical institutions outside the Cape were justifiable restraints. That Rycroft confronted these in a new policy of establishing regional gardens from 1957 onwards is to his credit.

In 1957 Kirstenbosch acquired two flora or wild flower reserves: the Tinie Versfeld Reserve at Darling, 100 kilometres (60 miles) north of Cape Town; and the Edith Stephens Cape flats Reserve near Philippi. The former was donated by Mr. Versfeld and comprised 22 ha. (54 acres) of his farm Slangkop. It was particularly important as it contained species native to the sandveld and swartland of the Cape. Chincherinchees were to be found here, as were such bulbous plants as *Babiana, Gladiolus* and *Spiloxene* and insectivorous *Drosera* species. The Cape flats reserve was much smaller than the Darling reserve, being only 3,6 ha. (8,9 acres). It had been bought from a grant awarded by the Cape Tercentenary Foundation to Miss Stephens, a lecturer in botany at the University of Cape Town from 1911 to 1940. Rich in algal flora, the reserve was especially valuable as an example of *Isoetes* vlei type.

The third regional garden acquired by Rycroft was an interesting coastal area overlooking Betty's Bay. It had been established as a nature reserve by Harold Nixon Porter, a businessman and prominent figure in the Botanical Society of South Africa. Opened by Professor Rycroft in 1955, the reserve originally bore the rather sentimental name, Shangri-La. In 1959 it was bequeathed to the National Botanic Gardens and was renamed the Harold Porter Botanic Garden. Covering 184 ha. (455 acres), in 1964 it was expanded to include the adjoining Disa Kloof.

This botanic garden was a very important addition as it contained a dense concentration of the south-western Cape's fynbos, having an impressive variety of ericas and proteas. But it lay within the Cape: indeed all the satellite gardens were in the Western Cape region. Only in 1967 did this situation change. In that year the Bloemfontein Municipality donated to the National Botanic Gardens 45 ha. (111 acres) of land some seven kilometres northwest of the city. On this site, which contained some small koppies, was established the Orange Free State Botanic Garden. Here grow the indigenous flora of the high altitudes of the Free State: acacias, the cabbage tree and the white stinkwood. Some of the semi-arid succulents and flowers featured at Worcester can also be grown there and such bulbous species as *Ammocharis* and *Brunsvigia* are also to be found there. A regular water supply remained a serious problem here until the mid-1980s, by which time some 40 000 people were visiting the garden annually.

Next there followed Natal. A botanic garden was established at Queen's Hill in Harrismith in 1967. Its present site was donated by the Municipality in 1969 and it became a regional garden with the title of the Drakensberg and Eastern Free State Botanic Garden. It was 114 ha. (280 acres) in extent, had several lakes and rose steeply up to the Platberg. Although containing some interesting botanical specimens, including berg lilies (*Galtonia candicans*) and grass bells (*Dierama* spp.) as well as a forest of old wood (*Leucosidea sericea*), this garden suffered from being remote. The lesson of Whitehill had not been learnt nor had the general advice of many eminent botanists of the past been taken.

In 1880 Sir William Thiselton-Dyer had asserted:

> "The site chosen should be conveniently accessible. A garden, however well managed and stocked with interesting and valuable plants, will be sure to languish if withdrawn in consequence of inconvenience of situation from the eye of the residents."

Thirty years later, Pearson had made the same point with reference to South Africa, warning that problems would arise if gardens were not situated near dense population centres. Although the Drakensberg Garden contained much of the flora of the berg and of the eastern Orange Free State, lack of support necessitated the garden passing into the hands of the Municipality in the mid-1980s.

Much more successful has been the progress made with the three other regional botanic gardens acquired by Kirstenbosch: Pietermaritzburg (1969), Nelspruit (1969) and Roodepoort (1985). In the late 1960s the old Pietermaritzburg Botanical Society finally relinquished its control of the city's botanic garden to the National Botanic Gardens. Although the garden had had some considerable success in the 1920s and 1930s, from the 1940s on the Society had struggled desperately because of lack of finance. The transfer of the garden to Kirstenbosch in 1969 was long overdue. It was renamed the Natal Botanic Garden, a title previously held by the Durban Botanic Garden. The local Municipality gave the deeds of the land to Kirstenbosch.

Considerable advances have been made in the Natal Botanic Garden under the curatorship of Mr. Peter Law and then Mr. Brian Tarr. Much of the alien tree vegetation has been cleared from the hillside and the Gimson bridge constructed across the Dorp Spruit, thus giving visitors access to the higher parts of the garden. In 1977 more land in this hill area was acquired for the garden. A botany school has also been established in the grounds. Trees are especially well suited to the soil of this garden and while it contains many species indigenous to Natal it also has an interesting collection of established foreign varieties of trees and has a fine collection of rhododendrons and camellias.

In 1969 the National Botanic Gardens acquired 154 ha. (380 acres) at Nelspruit which was donated by the Nelspruit Municipality and H. L. Hall and Sons. Here the Lowveld Botanic Garden was laid out in a very attractive setting at the confluence of the Crocodile and Nel Rivers, not far from the Kruger National Park. Visitors can see kiaat, marula and wild pear trees, Barberton daisies and a large collection of ferns.

The most recent addition to the National Botanic Gardens has been the Transvaal Botanic Garden, which was opened in November 1985 on land originally donated for a garden in 1982 by the Roodepoort Municipality. In this 50 ha. (125 acres) a garden is being established which will reflect the flora of the highveld. It contains the spectacular Roodepoort Falls and an area of dense riverine woodland. The garden also has an interpretative centre.

The concept of establishing a network of constituent botanic gardens centred on Kirstenbosch was a laudable one, but the establishment of these gardens must in itself be only a first step. Uniform planning of the whole and further development of their scientific role in particular have been to the fore in the 1980s.

To give a fuller picture, mention must be made of several wild flower reserves and botanic gardens which are independent of Kirstenbosch. Wild flower reserves are to be found at Clanwilliam, Hermanus, Paarl and Caledon, the latter dating back to 1927.

Certain botanic gardens remain independent of the National Botanic Gardens. At the Durban garden, for instance, Mr. Ken Wyman, the present Curator, building on the work of two previous curators, Frank Thorns and Ernest Thorp, has done much work to re-establish its former glory. The garden is particularly famous for its Ernest Thorp orchid house and for its *Encephalartos woodii*. Stellenbosch University's Hortus Botanicus is a small functional botanic garden which was established in 1923 and which is noted for its succulents, its herb and water gardens and such interesting plants as the giant *Welwitschia mirabilis* and the elephant's foot, *Dioscorea elephantipes*. Finally there is the Johannesburg Botanic Garden which, like its Durban counterpart, is a Municipal garden under the Parks Department. This garden is 125 ha. (300 acres) and lies alongside of the Emmarentia Dam. When established in 1969 it was planned as an international botanic garden, growing plants suitable for Johannesburg. It has its own herbarium and herb garden, and has a fine collection of roses in a part of the garden which used to be known as Van Riebeeck Park.

Education and research in the first 70 years

Perhaps Kirstenbosch's greatest successes and failures come in the fields of education and research. In conjunction with the Botanical Society of South Africa, the garden has done much to promote an interest in the preservation of the country's indigenous flora. In particular the regular publication since 1915 of the *Journal of the Botanical Society*, in 1975 renamed *Veld & Flora*, has helped stimulate a national awareness of indigenous plants far in excess of the Society's 15 000 or so members. Also significant have been the annual spring wild flower shows and plant sales held at Kirstenbosch by the Society and the distribution to Society members of Kirstenbosch seeds. The former was commenced in 1955 and the latter 21 years later. Plant sales are also conducted at several regional gardens. Since 1949 the Society has had its own office in the garden at which the public may buy botanical literature. This is appropriate, for without the Society's financial and moral support since 1913 it is doubtful whether Kirstenbosch would have survived.

Although in the past some believed that the National Botanic Gardens did not fulfil a satisfactory educational role, Kirstenbosch today does employ an Education Officer and has had in its grounds for many years a school at which the emphasis is on nature conservation and ecology. In 1923 the Cape's Department of Education appointed Letitia Starke as a teacher to give nature study classes out of doors at Kirstenbosch. This was done on the advice of Mrs. Louisa Bolus, the Curator of the Bolus herbarium, then housed in the garden. In 1933 Muriel Johns continued this practice with considerable success.

She was noted for her sense of humour and in particular for her ability to imitate bird calls. Six years later a nature study school was built in the garden. By 1955 the two teachers at the school taught some 12 000 school children who had occasional classes there. In 1969 the Cape Provincial Administration built a new school to cater for visiting classes of primary school children. In the early 1970s, a similar school to that at Kirstenbosch was built by the Natal Provincial Administration in the Pietermaritzburg Garden.

Less happy has been the saga of the establishment of a herbarium at the National Botanic Gardens. In 1923 a National Herbarium was founded in Pretoria under the control of the Department of Agriculture. Of this General Smuts said: "You want a Kew. What Kew is to England and the British empire this national herbarium must be to South Africa". Establishing this herbarium in Pretoria caused surprise at Kew and considerable resentment in Cape Town, voiced especially by the Cape Town press. It was pointed out that the 10-year-old National Botanic Gardens had no herbarium, an essential element for a botanic garden.

The following year the Bolus Herbarium and Library, which had become the university's property on Harry Bolus' death in 1911, was transferred from the University of Cape Town's premises in Queen Victoria Street in Cape Town to Kirstenbosch. Mrs. Louisa Bolus, the great-niece of Harry Bolus, was retained as Curator. This transfer was appropriate as it consolidated the special relationship between the university and the garden which had been forged through the linking of the directorship with a university chair. However, in 1934 the annual report of the Botanical Society contained the following ominous paragraph:

> "A report having been received that the University of Cape Town was discussing the removal of the Bolus Herbarium from the site which for 10 years it had occupied at Kirstenbosch, the council of the society protested to the university against the proposal as being prejudical to the work and interests of the National Botanic Gardens."

This decision by the university became what Compton later described as "a matter of acute controversy". It was true that Kirstenbosch lacked trained botanists: prior to 1933 there had been only the director. The very damp Kirstenbosch climate was detrimental to some herbarium specimens such as succulents. The heating facilities were primitive and had little effect. On 15 October 1925 H. G. Fourcade recorded in his diary details of a visit to the herbarium:

> "Mrs Bolus complains of the dampness of Kirstenbosch and showed me some sheets of Mesembs which although poisoned had become mildewed. I told her that the Tzitzikamma was at least equally damp but that I never had any trouble with my specimens there. It is possible that the walls of the herbarium are still damp and that the specimens are not sufficiently poisoned."

The transfer of the Bolus Herbarium and Library

to the Groote Schuur campus was completed in May 1938. It was a considerable body blow to inflict on the struggling institution of Kirstenbosch and it became obvious to Compton that the only course open to him was to start building up another herbarium from scratch. A new and more spacious building was begun and Kirstenbosch staff went out on collecting trips, often to remote areas. Alexander Middlemost, the Assistant Curator, became famous for his collecting adventures on a motorcycle. The South African Railways rallied to Kirstenbosch's aid, providing transport for specimens and for collectors. Herbaria in South Africa and overseas sent specimens to the new herbarium. In 1940 there were 32 cabinets containing 10 000 sheets under the care of Miss W. F. Barker and her two assistants; by 1953 this number had increased to 119 cabinets containing 58 000 specimens.

Criticism might be levelled that the new herbarium tended to divorce itself from the garden but this is not altogether fair as the staff was so small and limited in what it could achieve. During the Second World War the herbarium and the garden had a good link through Murray Ross Henderson who joined the staff of the herbarium and worked on the garden's cycad collection. In 1946 he returned to Singapore to take up his old post as Curator of the herbarium of the Colony's botanic garden.

In 1956 the old South African Museum in Cape Town decided to relinquish its herbarium, the oldest such institution in the country. This was offered to the National Herbarium in Pretoria, who hesitated in accepting it on account of a shortage of space. As Kirstenbosch were at that time building two new wings to the garden's herbarium, they had plenty of room and Pretoria's delay meant that Kirstenbosch was able to intervene and obtain the collection on permanent loan for themselves. This coup was followed through with great speed. The two new wings to the herbarium were opened by Professor Compton in October 1958 and the institution now officially bears his name. Under the energetic curatorship of Dr John Rourke, the herbarium is efficiently managed and is today the second largest such institution in South Africa. It also possesses a valuable collection of botanical literature.

As might be expected taxonomy has been carried on at Kirstenbosch for as long as the institution has had an herbarium. Professor Compton had a particular interest in taxonomy. The institution has also supported research through such awards as the Edward Muspratt Solly scholarship (established in 1924), the Smuts Memorial Fellowship (1951) and the J.W. Mathews Floating Trophy (1956) and the Harold Compton Prize (1980). Mention must also be made of the contribution to botany of the *Journal of South African Botany*, a journal founded in 1935 and edited by the director of the National Botanic Gardens. None the less a 1976 committee reported that "research does not actually exist at the National Botanic Gardens of South Africa".

Rivalry from the Highveld

In spite of perennial warfare and financial insecurity, an attempt was made to establish a botanic garden on the highveld in the nineteenth century. In 1873 the recently elected President Francois Burgers appointed eight people to a Botanical Committee in Pretoria. He followed this up by appointing John Hunter McLea as State Botanist for the South African Republic. McLea had just arrived in the Transvaal after an epic trek from Graaff-Reinet, which had taken him to Kimberley, Rustenburg and Pilgrim's Rest en route. As mentioned in a previous chapter McLea was one of those instrumental in establishing a botanic garden at Graaff-Reinet in 1872. President Burgers had been born near Graaff-Reinet and the two men had met there previous to McLea's moving to the Highveld.

Burgers was a man interested in the developments of his age and, as McLea was available, he determined that the Transvaal should have a botanic garden. In 1874 a grant of £100 was made to establish such an institution on 5 ha. (12 acres) in the southern part of Pretoria on a site which had been used as a camp by early white settlers.

It was proposed that McLea, as Curator, should establish four gardens within this area, representing the flora of the four hemispheres. This laudable scheme did not materialize and the botanic garden soon became a place for acclimatizing and distributing timber trees, especially eucalyptus, and an ornamental public park for the town's citizens. It was maintained partly through Government grant and partly through public subscriptions. In 1875 McLea decided to return to Graaff-Reinet and he was replaced by Otto Lincke. Little progress was made and the garden's fortunes steadily declined with those of the Republic's finances. When Shepstone annexed the Transvaal for Britain in April 1877 the Botanical Committee, under the chairmanship of Daniel Kisch, all resigned.

Shepstone was keen that botanical enterprise in the Transvaal should be encouraged. Of the garden itself, he wrote on 22 February 1879:

> "It appeared to me that this was both too ambitious and too unprofitable an aim for so young a country; but on the other hand the institution existed and it was necessary to keep it up."

Shepstone decided to establish a new "model farm and botanical gardens" some three kilometres (two miles) from the centre of Pretoria on the townlands. This he proposed would be 200 ha. (500 acres) in extent and would act as what today would be termed an agricultural college: educating the sons of farmers about trees and crops. Shepstone got as far as building a stone wall round 80 ha. (200 acres) and requesting a supply of suitable plants to be sent out from Britain by the Colonial Office. He was keen

that species of fruit should be sent as he claimed that the Transvaal had only two fruits and "they between four and five hundred miles apart".

The Colonial Office duly acquired four Wardian cases of plants and bulbs from Kew. These were valued at £25 and were despatched from London in November 1880. By the time they arrived in Natal en route for the Transvaal, the first Anglo-Boer War had broken out. In Durban George Cato discovered the cases and wrote to G. Baillie, Curator of the Pietermaritzburg Botanic Garden, of their existence. Baillie, determined on hijacking the consignment, wrote to the Natal Colonial Secretary:

> "Permit me to suggest that [the Wardian cases] should be given over to the curator of the gardens here to be planted out, on the understanding that at some future time portions of the plants might be forwarded to Pretoria as required when communications be opened." (Natal Archives: Shepstone papers)

This was done in March 1881; the plants never reached their destination. With the end of the British annexation that year Shepstone's scheme came to an end and the old botanic garden in Pretoria quickly deteriorated, until by the mid-1880s it was little more than an open space. In 1886 Melrose House was built overlooking the site.

In 1889 a revival of the garden was proposed and in March 1890 plans were put before the Executive Council of the Volksraad. Georges Heys, the owner of Melrose House and a local entrepreneur, was paid £1 125 to establish a park and lay on a water supply. An overseer's house, complete with spire, and a central ornamental pond were built and five years later a tea room and bandstand were added to the attractions of what was now called Burgers Park. On 31 August 1898 an orange tree was planted in the park to commemorate the accession of Queen Wilhelmina of the Netherlands. By then the Pretoria garden had followed most of the old botanic gardens of the Cape by becoming little more than an attractive public park.

In 1954 the appropriate step was taken of placing a statue of President Burgers in Pretoria's first botanic garden. A suggestion that a statue of President Kruger also be placed in the grounds came to nothing as it was pointed out that Burgers and Kruger were arch-rivals.

The South African Republic had no department of agriculture, although from 1896 it did have a State Veterinarian, mainly to deal with rinderpest. From 1894 the State had also had a State Museum which was situated in Pretoria. In 1898 a Dutch woman called Reino Leendertz (later Mrs. Pott-Leendertz) was appointed to the museum staff, thus becoming the first woman civil servant in the State. She was a trained pharmacist and botanist and was in charge of the new Transvaal Museum and Zoological Gardens Herbarium, the foundation of which was a collection of Rudolf Schlechter's specimens. After an absence from South Africa between 1901 and 1904 she returned to her old job in what was now the

Transvaal Museum Herbarium. From here she often went out collecting on a bicycle. Over the years the collection at this herbarium grew slowly but steadily. Ultimately in 1956, when it contained 40 000 specimens, it was transferred to the National Herbarium in Pretoria.

A moribund Pretoria Botanic Garden and a small Transvaal herbarium could not rival the supremacy of the Cape for botanical enterprise in the late nineteenth century. In the opening decade of the new century, however, an embryonic botanical section of the new Transvaal Colonial Department of Agriculture heralded the beginning of what was to become a formidable rival to Kirstenbosch.

In 1903 Joseph Burtt Davy, a Kewite who had lived for a period in the United States of America, became the Transvaal Department of Agriculture's agrostologist and botanist. He had a small office in the old Volkstem building in Pretoria and here, later assisted by Sydney Margaret Stent, he established the Transvaal Colonial Herbarium. Two years later he was joined by Dr. I. B. Pole Evans who was in charge of plant pathology, carrying on research in western Pretoria. The two strands of botanical endeavour were formally amalgamated in 1913, following Burtt Davy's retirement, into one Division of Botany and Plant Pathology which was part of the Department of Agriculture. The new division was based at Vrede Huis in Vermeulen Street, Pretoria, where a small botanic garden was established.

The year 1913 also saw the establishment of Kirstenbosch and the demise of the old Durban Botanic Garden. It was significant that the government chose to associate the Natal Herbarium with Pole Evans' division and not with the new National Botanic Gardens, which at that time had no herbarium at all. With the acquisition of Wood's Natal herbarium, the new division began to "assume a national character".

When Parliament was debating the establishment of Kirstenbosch in 1913, Sir Lionel Phillips skirted the problem of the existing botanical laboratory in Pretoria and merely remarked that a laboratory at Kirstenbosch would be supplementary to the one in Pretoria. Sir Percy FitzPatrick, who represented a Pretoria constituency, had mixed loyalties but asserted firmly: "Let there be no local jealousies in this matter".

The Division of Botany and Plant Pathology quickly consolidated its position as the principal institution of botanical research and publication in the country. In 1919 the *Kew Bulletin* spoke of:

"The enlightenment of outlook in matters connected with the bearing of scientific knowledge on practical affairs, which experience has taught us to expect on the part of the government of the Union of South Africa."

Evidence of the truth of this is easy to find in these years. In 1918 the Division began the *Memoirs of the*

Botanical Survey of South Africa series; in 1920 the *Flowering Plants of South Africa* series was started; and in 1921 publication commenced of the botanical, and largely taxonomic journal, *Bothalia*, so named in honour of the late Premier General Louis Botha. Pole Evans was behind these three initiatives. As mentioned, in 1923 the National Herbarium was established in Pretoria. Its primary function was to serve the botanical survey project. E. P. Phillips was appointed the first Curator.

The inevitable proposal that a botanic garden be attached to this herbarium followed in the mid-1940s. This was eventually achieved in conjunction with the University of Pretoria and under the direction of R. A. Dyer, Phillips' successor. The former wrote later:

"Kirstenbosch served the needs of the winter rainfall region of the Union, and a similar institution to serve the summer rainfall area was an obvious necessity. That it should be complementary to the National Herbarium also seemed obvious."

At the official opening of the Pretoria National Botanic Garden on 23 October 1958 the Secretary for Agriculture, P. K. le Roux, said: "Kirstenbosch cannot feature the whole of the Union's flora. No single institution could do so". By this time a separate Division of Botany had been in existence for five years. Not until 1961 was the present title, the Botanical Research Institute (BRI), adopted. Today the National Herbarium has some half million botanical specimens, mainly of southern African species. It has satellite herbaria in Durban, Grahamstown, Kimberley, Stellenbosch and Windhoek. The botanic garden, of 77 ha. (190 acres), has a well-developed, luxuriant indigenous collection divided into the biomes to be found in the subcontinent. It has its own hot and shade houses and a collection of over 500 species of South African trees. The Mary Gunn Library has possibly the finest botanical and botanical history collections on the African continent. But it is especially in the field of research that the Botanical Research Institute has made its name: as well as taxonomy, taxicology, mycology, quantitative ecology, plant anatomy and cyto-genetics, the institute works on economic botany and continues to publish *Bothalia* and the Botanical Surveys.

The Botanical Research Institute has achieved an international reputation for research. This is symbolized by the South African Liaison Officer maintained at the Royal Botanic Gardens, Kew, initially by the Division of Botany and later by the institute. The first "botanical assistant for the Union of South Africa at Kew" was appointed in 1919; she was Miss A. G. Corbishley, a former student of Professor J. W. Bews. Today the Liaison Officer acts as an unofficial ambassador for South African botany at Kew. The position gives invaluable experience to promising botanists.

POSTSCRIPT: "21ST CENTURY CHALLENGE"

Professor J. N. (Kobus) Eloff was appointed Director of the National Botanic Gardens with effect from 1 August 1983. Two months before this, as Director Designate, he made it clear that under his leadership a major re-examination of the purpose and functioning of the National Botanic Gardens would be initiated. Writing in *Veld & Flora* in June, he singled out one specific target for his attention:

"Although all the previous Directors were interested in advanced research, I do not think that it has yet reached a satisfactory scope at Kirstenbosch. My predecessors have established the infrastructure of a highly efficient administration, horticulture and regional gardens upon which an active research programme can now be based. Because it has been stated that it is actually the research that distinguishes a botanic garden from a park or nature reserve, I hope that I will have the support of the Botanical Society members in my efforts to extend the scope and depth of research without neglecting all the other important functions of the National Botanic Gardens."

Over the next two years Professor Eloff formulated a scheme to give the institution a more scientific orientation. By September 1984, the "mission" of the National Botanic Gardens had been formulated: "To promote knowledge and appreciation of southern African flora and to undertake the *ex situ* conservation of threatened plants."

In December 1984 *Veld & Flora* carried a special report by Professor Eloff entitled "Kirstenbosch—Quo Vadis?" This was followed up by a second report, "Conservation through education—a prime function of the National Botanic Gardens", which appeared in the September 1985 issue of the journal. But most significant of all was Professor Eloff's inaugural lecture as Harold Pearson Professor of Botany at the University of Cape Town, which was delivered on 13 March 1985 under the title "Botanic gardens: Victorian relic or 21st century challenge?" The concluding section of this book will examine Professor Eloff's objectives for the National Botanic Gardens and the successes which have been achieved to date.

Having been controlled by a series of government ministries, in 1981 the National Botanic Gardens passed under the jurisdiction of the Department of Environmental Affairs. Subsequently, under the provisions of the Forest Act, Number 122 of 1984, the institution became a statutory board: that is, an autonomous state-aided institution. In accordance with Professor Eloff's own ideals, part nine of the Forest Act states clearly that the object of the National Botanic Gardens must be the conservation of and research into the flora of the southern African subcontinent as a whole. Six specific roles were assigned to it:

1. To collect and cultivate in the National Botanic Gardens plants indigenous to the subcontinent.

2. To undertake and promote research in connection with plants and related matters and make indigenous plant material available for research.
3. To study and cultivate endangered plant species.
4. To investigate and utilize, and promote the utilization of, the economic potential of indigenous plants.
5. To promote an appreciation of indigenous plants among the public.
6. To establish non-indigenous plants for comparative studies and educational purposes.

It is interesting to note that the last-mentioned role involves the growing of certain non-indigenous plants. This mandate, coupled with Professor Eloff's mission, gives the institution a broad base on which to operate and does not tie the institution to narrow and perhaps chauvinistic confines.

The problems which beset Professor Eloff were numerous. They varied from a lack of staff, of adequate funding, of research and education facilities and of operational planning to a need to develop the regional gardens along more scientific and educational lines. Concerning this last problem, in 1986 the Board of Trustees approved a policy of systematically stimulating the development of each existing regional garden to its maximum potential. In that year it was also proposed that responsibility for matters of education, information and plant utilization should be transferred from the central National Botanic Gardens office at Kirstenbosch to the individual gardens' administrations.

It is expected that the administrative reforms which came with the new dispensation will also benefit these gardens. The old position of Director was reconstituted as Executive Director, thus enabling the creation of a number of directorships. Dr Daan Botha became Director: Gardens with the activities of all gardens under his control. Dr Fiona Getliffe Norris was appointed as Director: Education/Information and Mr Braam Jordaan became Director: Administration. Mr Johan Grobler became Director: Kirstenbosch in November 1986. The posts of Director: Research and Director: Plant Utilization have not yet been filled. As the regional gardens mature, garden directors will be allocated to each garden to ensure coordination of the institution's diverse functions. The final stage of these administrative reforms will be an upper echelon of highly trained and motivated directors under the Executive Director.

Although this reform plan has yet to be completed, the staffing structure at Kirstenbosch itself has been rationalized to produce greater staff efficiency. In 1987 Professor Eloff stated quite bluntly that the National Botanic Gardens should be run on business principles, i.e. objectives should be formulated clearly and resources should be used to attain the objectives.

After careful consideration of the viability of all the different botanic gardens, the Board of the National Botanic Gardens decided that in one, the Drakensberg Botanic Garden, the objectives of the National Botanic Gardens could not be realized on a cost effective basis and so it was resolved that this garden should become a wild flower garden and be returned to the Municipality of Harrismith, which originally donated the land.

Professor Eloff's approach since he assumed his position has always been that each of the four primary functions which he enumerated in his inaugural lecture—namely horticulture, research, plant utilization and education—must justify its existence. In concluding this book it is fitting to give brief consideration to each, for they paint a rosy picture of what is being achieved today at Kirstenbosch.

HORTICULTURE

This is naturally the most highly developed of the National Botanic Gardens' functions for it is the aesthetic of the "daisy extravaganza" and the like which first attract many visitors to Kirstenbosch or to one of the other National Botanic Gardens. Approximately a third of South Africa's nearly 24 000 higher plants (about 7 000 species) are to be found at Kirstenbosch. Today more than 600 000 people visit the garden annually and, as Professor Eloff has rightly pointed out, it has not only many more visitors per year than the Kruger National Park but is also one of Cape Town's top tourist attractions. To enhance Kirstenbosch's beauty, it has been proposed that as many as possible of the garden's central buildings should be moved out to the garden's boundaries. A proposal was also made to build an unobtrusive amphitheatre in the garden as an idyllic setting for the performing arts, but after this proposal was discussed at a public meeting it was decided not to proceed.

The creation of an attractive garden, however, is only a means to the end of botanical or environmental education. Mr John Winter, Head of Horticulture at Kirstenbosch, and his horticulturists have laid out a vast number of indigenous plants according to aesthetic, scientific and educational principles, and where possible they have also preserved genetic variables of the flora, so that visitors can admire and learn at the same time. In many cases these plants are threatened species which, as will be illustrated shortly, are being preserved and cultivated in the garden.

The practicality of imparting horticultural information to the general public was a matter of concern to the Board during the mid-1980s. Much research information was lost because it was never published. In March 1987, therefore, *Veld & Flora* became a joint publication of the National Botanic Gardens and the Botanical Society. The existing editor, Lieutenant-Commander Richard Geary-Cooke, was joined by Professor Eloff and Dr Daan Botha as joint editors. Mr Heinz Engelhardt remained as production editor. An additional eight pages were added to the journal and more emphasis was placed on horticulture and research findings than previously. Other themes covered in the new *Veld & Flora* are flora conservation, education and news from Botanical Society branches and from the National Botanic Gardens.

Future horticultural possibilities at the institution include courses leading to a National Botanic Gardens diploma or certificate in horticulture, in which the emphasis would be on the use of indigenous material; and the establishment of small thematic gardens, such as gardens of threatened plants, or historical plants, or parasitic plants, or economically valuable plants; and the laying out of an arboretum.

RESEARCH

Under Professor Eloff's guidance, research has assumed a much more significant role at the National Botanic Gardens than previously. This has not occurred at the expense of the two aspects of research which existed before 1983: with the experienced Dr John Rourke at its head, the Compton Herbarium maintains its work on the Proteaceae as well as on such plant types as *Bulbinella, Cyanella, Eriospermum, Hessea* and *Strumaria*. Work is also carried out on the pollination biology of *Diascia*. The Compton Herbarium must be classified as one of the great herbaria of the southern hemisphere. It has the potential and the available material to extend its scope of research on south-western Cape flora, much of which is still carried on overseas, but financial constraints remain a stumbling block to such expansion.

It has been in the new fields of research that Professors Eloff and his colleagues have generated most excitement in the scientific world. There are four prerequisites for a new research programme. The first of these is an enthusiastic promotor of the concept of the National Botanic Gardens as a truly research-orientated, as distinct from mainly horticultural, institution. This enthusiasm has been provided by the Executive Director. As the former Professor of Botany at the University of the Orange Free State, his natural inclinations as an academic are towards research and education, and it is in no small part due to his perseverance that such a promising start has been made to expanding the research field in the last five years. The second prerequisite is adequate financing of research facilities and research projects. In the last five years the research budget at the National Botanic Gardens has steadily increased. Funding has come not only from direct central government grants, with increasing support from the Department of Environment Affairs, but also from private donations, contract research and extra-governmental bodies, such as the Council for Scientific and Industrial Research, the University of Cape Town and the South African Nature Foundation. There is also the prospect of the endangered plant unit earning significant sums through its work.

Closely connected with funding is the matter of staffing. The 1976 Meiring Naude committee conceded that the National Botanic Gardens required a research staff 10 times the size of that which existed at the time. While research has doubly benefited by being allocated a greater share of the institution's increased funding, in proportion to the total workforce the National Botanic Gardens' scientific establishment is still considerably less than that of other great botanic gardens of the world, such as the Royal Botanic Gardens, Kew, and the Missouri Botanical Garden in the United States. In part the difficulty has been alleviated by the appointment of a number of postgraduate students with two- to three-year appointments at the institution and by the presence of guest researchers.

The fourth essential for an extensive research programme is modern facilities. As early as 1922 Professor Compton had pressed for a laboratory to be built at Kirstenbosch. Yet by the early 1980s there was no laboratory research facility at all. It was not until 1986 that a properly furnished and equipped laboratory was opened when two semi-detached houses were converted. The furniture was donated by the Botanical Society and much of the apparatus was bought from grants made by the Council for Scientific and Industrial Research and the University of Cape Town. Nearly a quarter of a million rand was given for the project by the Rowland and Leta Hill Trust through the South African Nature Foundation. The building was named the Threatened Plant Research Laboratory and was opened by the State President, Mr P. W. Botha, in September 1986. Once money is available, it is intended that these embryonic laboratory facilities will be expanded into a modern research complex.

One new direction for research at the National Botanic Gardens was signalled in the early 1980s when the Cape Provincial Administration decided that in future the conservation *ex situ*—that is, outside their natural environment—of threatened or endangered plants should be carried out at Kirstenbosch. So grave has the prospect become for the survival of certain plants in their natural habitat that their only lifeline is to be propagated at Kirstenbosch. Compiling a list of threatened plants in order of importance has been given priority and a national seed bank is being established in an attempt to preserve threatened plants in their seed form. Plant pathology, biochemistry and specific projects on the tissue culture of threatened plants that cannot be easily propagated by other means are being investigated. Plants under scrutiny at present include

Audouinia capitata, Clivia miniata, Encephalartos woodii, Nerine sarniensis, Protea odorata, Raspalia trigyna, Sandersonia aurantiaca, Staavia dodii and *Veltheimia bracteata.* Problems concerning aspects such as the maintenance of the genetic variability, breaking of seed dormancy, keeping seed viable over long periods, seed-borne diseases and the rooting of cuttings are being investigated in this important and expanding field of research.

PLANT UTILIZATION

Plant utilization concerns the promotion of the possible economic potential of indigenous plants and of making these plants available to the public with the intention of fostering an appreciation of them and so reducing pressure on them in the wild; by e.g. selecting and hybridizing plants. As stated earlier, the growing of "economics" had taken place at Kirstenbosch in the 1920s and early 1930s, but the scope of these experiments had been limited. Today, with advanced chemical investigations, the attempt to exploit indigenous plants for their possible horticultural, agricultural and medical use has been reinvigorated at the National Botanic Gardens.

The general public's awareness of indigenous plant life and its potential has been stimulated in two ways: the exhibition of indigenous plants at national and international flower shows; and the supply of indigenous seed and plants to the public and to other institutions and organisations.

Between 1976 and 1987 the National Botanic Gardens' entries at the annual Chelsea International Flower Show in London have won 10 gold medals. It has also regularly won the coveted Wilkinson Sword for the best overseas exhibit. Similar success has been gained at other such flower shows, as for example that at Southport in August 1985. In South Africa the Botanical Society's annual spring wild flower show has been held for over 30 years, attracting a large number of specialist exhibitors. In 1984 3 000 people visited the four-day show where over 300 species were being judged, comprising 34% bulbous plants, 25% *Protea*, 19% *Erica*, 18% perennial shrubs, trees and climbers and 4% orchids. In 1983 a considerable boost was given to popularizing indigenous plants by the exhibition Flora '83, held in the Good Hope Centre in Cape Town. This was organized by the National Botanic Gardens, the Botanical Society and the South African Nature Foundation and over the show's three days the total number of visitors was about 70 000. In 1988, as part of Kirstenbosch's 75th anniversary celebrations, a similar extravaganza, to be called Kirstenbosch 75, will be held.

If the flower shows draw attention to the glory of the South African floral kingdom, the supply of seed and plants to the public provides a very practical way of preserving indigenous plant life from extinction. The National Botanic Gardens' Index Seminum lists hundreds of seed types which are available to botanic gardens, universities and research institutions worldwide. In addition, through the Botanical Society, the National Botanic Gardens annually provides more than 60 000 packets of seeds free to members of the Society.

The spectre of unfair state competition which threatened nineteenth-century nurserymen has been laid to rest after an agreement between the National Botanic Gardens and the South African Nurserymen's Association that the National Botanic Gardens will supply only plants not generally available to the public. Indeed the nursery trade has benefited considerably from the approximately 500 different indigenous seed species offered to it for sale by the National Botanic Gardens. As the annual Government grant to the National Botanic Gardens falls short of what is needed, the income from such sales is vital to the institution.

Much needed income is also gained from the annual plant sale at Kirstenbosch. Since the inception of this event in September 1976 the stock of more than 700 indigenous plant species offered for sale through the Botanical Society has more than quadrupled and net annual receipts amount to about R95 000, with cycads, tree ferns and succulents being in especially high demand. Regional gardens also offer excess stock for sale, thereby stimulating in their own areas public interest in the cultivation of indigenous plants.

The supply of indigenous seed and plants has increased dramatically in the last five years and has entailed considerable organizing effort on the part of the gardens and members of the Botanical Society.

EDUCATION

The National Botanic Gardens has as one of its functions the dissemination of information on plant life, on the role of plants in the environment and on plant cultivation. It also has a particular part to play in promoting a greater appreciation of southern Africa's indigenous flora. This educational function is approached in different ways and at different levels. The schools in the Kirstenbosch and Natal Botanic Gardens continue to flourish and to offer formal education to many thousands of school children annually. In addition, an education officer organizes less formal educational activities. Worksheets are compiled and competitions organized on indigenous or conservation-related topics. More than 27 000 people of all ages and races were handled by the education officer at Kirstenbosch in 1987. Many guided tours are organized, some of which are led by members of the Botanical Society, and self-guided tours have also been established.

On a wider scale, the Botanical Society plays a very important role in educating the general public. With 11 branches and 15 000 members in all four provinces as well as thousands of overseas members, they do invaluable work. Excursions, lectures and slide shows are organized and, as discussed earlier, plant sales, seed distribution and flower shows are undertaken by members. *Veld & Flora* has done more than perhaps any other journal or periodical to create public awareness of southern Africa's flora; indeed it has been in the vanguard of the campaign to eradicate alien vegetation. For the enthusiastic amateur, the society also publishes a series of wild flower guides. These and many other botanical works are sold at the thriving bookshop which the society runs in its new premises beside the resited entrance to Kirstenbosch.

An important component of this education/information role has been the publication of research findings in the *Journal of South African Botany* and in the irregular series of monographs published as supplementary volumes to this journal. In 1984 the journal was amalgamated with the *South African Journal of Botany* and continued to be edited from Kirstenbosch. A new series of specialized monographs and major works on southern African flora was then founded. Although this was called the *Annals of Kirstenbosch Botanic Gardens*, the volume numbering followed on from the old supplementary volumes.

The aim of this new series is to publish substantial volumes on research relating to southern Africa plants. It is not restricted to purely botanical research, but also embraces the results of horticultural experimentation such as the long awaited Lachenalia handbook by Graham Duncan which is due out in 1988 and which is one of a series of titles which will be published in 1988 to commemorate the 75th anniversary of the National Botanic Gardens. Other works which will mark this event are *Pelargoniums of Southern Africa, Volume 3* by J. J. A. van der Walt, P. J. Vorster and Ellaphie Ward-Hilhorst and a revision of Watsonia by Peter Goldblatt. In addition there is this present one which is based on historical research of botanical gardens. The Annals series was successfully launched by *The Moraeas of Southern Africa* by Peter Goldblatt and Fay Anderson and *The Botany of the Southern Natal Drakensberg*, by O. M. Hilliard and B. L. Burtt, both which were enthusiastically received by reviewers.

The National Botanic Gardens has also published a number of smaller works dealing with the southern African flora, ranging from indigenous herbs to haworthias, Cape Peninsula ferns and *Plectranthus*. There are also several horticultural pamphlets available with practical advice on subjects such as coastal grasses, bulbous plants and the cultivation of proteas.

It has recently been revealed that the average age of a visitor to Kirstenbosch is just 18 and a half years old. While this is very encouraging for potential future support for the institution, it also poses a challenge to Dr Fiona Getliffe Norris, the Director of Education/Information. Formal education is relatively straightforward; less formal education work may need considerable initiative on her part to succeed.

In 1986 a survey was undertaken to find out the needs and opinions of visitors to Kirstenbosch. The results were generally favourable to the institution and over 90% of the respondents felt that the general appearance of the garden was good. Although still a minority, the number of visitors who came to learn about plants had increased since the last survey was carried out in 1973. The fact that only 51% considered that educationally important non-indigenous plants should be grown illustrates the growth of interest in indigenous vegetation. However, in reaction to replies to one question, Professor Eloff noted:

> "It was surprising that only 62 per cent of the visitors agreed that an information/interpretative centre was urgently required. This is a danger sign, indicating that many people visit Kirstenbosch just for relaxation and not really with the intention to learn something about plants."

Although it is 140 years since the old Cape Town Botanic Garden was established, this is one danger which would superficially seem to remain. Professor Eloff, however, is in a happier position than Mr McGibbon or Professor MacOwan. He has a professional staff under his direction, he has an annual budget of over R7 million, he has a staff complement of some 400, he has the foresight to realize that substantial sums will be needed to promote the National Botanic Gardens as a research and educational centre and he has the incentive to capitalize on growing urbanization and an increase in general levels of education.

The 75th anniversary celebrations may thus be said to complete the pioneering stage on the way to Kirstenbosch. In conclusion, we would say of Kirstenbosch what the great botanist Sir William Thiselton-Dyer said 80 years ago of Kew in the introduction to Bean's history of that institution—may the reader join with those who have played their part in the work in the final coda: FLOREAT KIRSTENBOSCH.

Select bibliography

Since nineteenth century botanic gardens in the Cape and Natal were recipients of grants from their respective colonial governments, the annual curators' reports were often printed in official publications. In the Cape Colony they appeared in *Annexures to votes and proceedings of the House of Assembly*. In the Colony of Natal, from the mid-1860s onwards, they were to be found in the *Natal Government Gazette*. For those years in which annual reports were not officially published we used those annual reports printed in pamphlet form or in newspapers. As well as the annual reports, the colonial governments occasionally published documents relating to the botanic gardens. The most significant of these are "Report of the select committee on The Botanical Garden" (Cape Colony, 1856 and 1880) and "Correspondence and Reports relative to the state of Botanic Enterprise in Natal, 1882" (Pietermaritzburg, 1884). The Natal Botanic Gardens Commission of 1890–91 never reported, but a copy of Shepstone's memorandum relating to the commission can be found in the *Natal Mercury*, 9 December 1898.

For manuscript material we relied heavily on those museums and libraries acknowledged in the preface. This material compromises mainly minute and memorandum books and correspondence relating to the local botanic gardens. As well as in museums, manuscript material is to be found in the Grahamstown City Hall, the Natal Archives, Pietermaritzburg, and in the Natal Herbarium, Durban. The last of these contains a useful collection of papers assembled by Mr. R. G. Strey. The Killie Campbell Africana Library, Durban houses a large collection of manuscript material relating to the Durban and Pietermaritzburg Botanic Gardens. Copies of the correspondence between Natal and Kew Gardens are to be found in this library under the classification "Strey papers". In the text of this volume reference to this correspondence is followed by "K.C" with the number of the letter.

NEWSPAPERS AND JOURNALS

Agricultural Journal (Natal)
Berea Pictorial
Bothalia
Bulletin of Miscellaneous Information, Royal Gardens, Kew (Kew Bulletin)
Cape Argus
Cape Monitor
Cape Monthly Magazine
Cape of Good Hope Literary Magazine
Cape Town Mail
Fort Beaufort Advocate
Garden History
Gardeners' Chronicle
Graaff-Reinet Herald
Graham's Town Journal
Grocott's Penny Mail
Journal of Botany
Journal of the University of Durban-Westville
Kaffrarian Watchman
Literary Review
Natal Colonist
Natal Mercury
Natal Observer
Natal Witness
Natalia
Natalian
Park Administration
Quarterly Bulletin of the South African Library
Report on the progress and condition of the Royal Gardens at Kew (Kew Report)
South African Commercial Advertiser
South African Journal of Science
Times of Natal
Transactions of the South African Philosophical Society
Veld & Flora

BOOKS, PAMPHLETS AND ARTICLES

ADAMSON, J. C., 1857. The South African Institution. *The Cape Monthly Magazine* 2(9): 154–6.

ALLEN, V., 1971. *Kruger's Pretoria*. A. A. Balkema. Cape Town.

ALLEN, D. E., 1969. *The Victorian fern craze, A history of pteridomania*. Hutchinson. London.

BARBER, M. E., 1963. Wanderings in South Africa by sea and land, 1879. *Quarterly Bulletin of the South African Library* 18(1): 6–11.

BAYER, A., (ed.), 1979. *Flower Paintings of Katharine Saunders*. Tongaat Group Ltd., Natal.

BAYER, A. N., 1971. Aspects of Natal's Botanical History. *South African Journal of Science* 67(8): 401–411.

BOTANICAL GARDENS IN SOUTH AFRICA, 1895. *Kew Bulletin* 99: 49–53.

BRADLOW, E. and F., 1951. *Thomas Bowler of the Cape of Good Hope*. A. A. Balkema. Cape Town.

BRADLOW, F. R., 1965. Baron von Ludwig and the Ludwig's-burg Gardens. *Quarterly Bulletin of the South African Library* 18: 110–117.

BROCKWAY, L. H., 1979. *Science and colonial expansion: The role of the British Royal Botanic Society*. Academic Press. New York.

BUCHANAN, Rev. J., 1875. *Ferns of Natal*. Private. Durban.

BURCHELL, W. J., 1810. *Travels into the interior of southern Africa* (Facsimile reprint, Batchworth Press; Cape Town, 1953).

CAPE HERBARIUM, 1895. *Kew Bulletin* 107: 303–305.

CAPE OF GOOD HOPE OFFICIAL HAND-BOOK, 1886. Cape Government. Cape Town.

CAPE TOWN BOTANIC GARDEN, 1892. *Kew Bulletin* 61: 10–14.

CHILD, D., 1979. *A merchant family in early Natal, diaries and letters of Joseph and Marianne Churchill.* A. A. Balkema. Cape Town.

COMPTON, R. H., 1965. *Kirstenbosch: Garden for a Nation.* Cape Town.

DYER, R. A., 1960. The opening of the Pretoria National Botanic Garden. *Bothalia* VII(II): 391–401.

ELIOVSON, S., 1979. *Garden beauty of Southern Africa.* Macmillan South Africa. Johannesburg.

ELOFF, J. N., 1984. Kirstenbosch—Quo Vadis?, (special report). *Veld & Flora* 70: iv.

ELOFF, J. N., 1985*(a)*. *Botanic gardens: Victorian relic or 21st century challenge?* UCT inaugural lecture.

ELOFF, J. N., 1985*(b)*. Conservation through education—a prime function of the National Botanic Gardens, (special report). *Veld & Flora* 71: vii.

ELOFF, J. N., 1986*(a)*. The Kirstenbosch visitor —who, what, where and why? *Veld & Flora* 72: 75–66.

ELOFF, J. N., 1986*(b)*. Ontginning van die groen goud van Suid-Afrika, *SA Tydskrif vir Natuurwetenskap en Tegnologie* 52: 58–60.

ELOFF, J. N., 1987. The establishment of the threatened plant laboratory at Kirstenbosch. *South African Journal of Science* 73.

ELOFF, J. N., GROBLER, P. J., JORDAAN, A. W., ROURKE, J. P., BOTHA, D. J., WINTER, J. H. S., KRUGER, P., and DAVIDSON, D. C., 1985. *National Botanic Gardens, Corporate Plan,* Kirstenbosch.

ERGATES, 1903. A chat with J. Medley Wood, A.L.S. *Agricultural Journal,* VI(II): 345–347.

FOURCADE, H. G., 1889. *Report on the Natal Forests.* Natal Government. Pietermaritzburg.

GORDON-BROWN, A., 1975. *Pictorial Africana.* Cape Town.

GREEN, L., 1951. *Grow lovely, growing old.* Timmins. Cape Town.

GUNN, M. and CODD, L. E., (eds.), 1981. *Botanical exploration of Southern Africa.* A. A. Balkema. Cape Town.

HADFIELD, M., 1960. *A history of British gardening.* Spring Books. London.

HATTERSLEY, A. F., 1940. The Natalians. Shuter & Shooter. Pietermaritzburg.

HATTERSLEY, A. F., 1950. The British settlement of Natal, C.U.P.

HENDERSON, W. P. M., 1904. *Durban: Fifty years' municipal history.* Robinson & Co. Durban.

HENNING, C. G., 1975. *Graaff-Reinet, A cultural history, 1786–1886.* T. V. Bulpin. Cape Town.

HOLDEN, Rev. W. C., 1855. *History of the Colony of Natal, South Africa.* Private. London.

HOOKER, Sir J. D., (ed.), 1896. *Journal of the Rt. Hon. Sir Joseph Banks.* Macmillan. London.

"HORTULANUS", 1857. A Cape botanical garden, as it should be. *Cape Monthly Magazine* 2(9): 173–180.

HYAMS, E. and MACQUITTY, W., 1985. *Great botanical gardens of the world.* Bloomsbury Books. London.

IMMELRAM, S. R. F. M. (ed.). 1969. A visit to Cape Town in 1853, The journal of G. G. Belcher. *Quarterly Bulletin of the South African Library* 23: 129.

JOELSON, A., 1940. *South African yesterdays.* Lustica Press. Cape Town.

KARSTEN, M. C., 1951. *The Old Company's Garden.* Miller. Cape Town.

KILLICK, D. J. B., 1979. The contribution of the B.R.I. to botany in South Africa. *Bothalia* 12(4): 740–742.

LAIDLER, P. W., c. 1926. *A tavern of the ocean.* Maskew Miller. Cape Town.

LAIDLER, P. W., 1939. *The growth and government of Cape Town.* Unie-Volkspers. Cape Town.

LIFE AT THE CAPE, BY A LADY, 1870. *Literary Review* new series 1.

LIGHTON, Conrad, 1960. *Cape Floral Kingdom.* Juta & Co. Cape Town.

McCRACKEN, Donal P., 1984. The development of botanic institutions in nineteenth-century Natal and West Africa. *Journal of the University of Durban-Westville* 4(3): 107–115.

McCRACKEN, Donal P., 1986. William Keit and the Durban Botanic Gardens. *Bothalia* 16(7): 71–5.

McCRACKEN, Donal P., 1987. Durban Botanic Gardens, Natal, 1851–1913. *Garden History* 15(1): 64–73.

McCRACKEN, Eileen M., with COLLERAN, John, 1977. "The Japanese garden, Tully, Kildare". *Garden History* 5(1): 30–42.

McCRACKEN, Eileen M., 1971. *The palm house and botanic gardens, Belfast.* Ulster Architectural Heritage Society. Belfast.

McCRACKEN, Eileen M., 1979. The Botanic Garden, Trinity College, Dublin. *Garden History* 7(1): 86–91.

McCRACKEN, Eileen M., 1980. The Cork Botanic Gardens, *Garden History* 8(1): 41–46.

McCRACKEN, Eileen M. with NELSON, E. Charles, 1987. *The brightest jewel: A history of the National Botanic Gardens, Glasnevin, Dublin.* Boethius Press. Kilkenny.

McKEN, M. J., 1869. *The Ferns of Natal.* Private. Pietermaritzburg.

MAXWELL, W. A., 1979. *The great exhibition at Grahamstown, December 1898–January 1899.* Private. Grahamstown.

MENTZEL, O. F. (translated by H. J. Mandelbrote), 1921. *A geographical and topographical description of the Cape of Good Hope,* part 1, first series, no. 4. Van Riebeeck Society, Cape Town.

MURRAY, J., (ed.), 1953. *In mid-victorian Cape Town.* A. A. Balkema. Cape Town.

NOBLE, (ed.), 1871. Souvenirs du Cap de Bonne Esperance par A. Haussman, 1866. *Literary Review* new series 2: 84.

OBERHOLSTER, J. J., 1972. *The historical monuments of South Africa.* National Monuments Council. Cape Town.

OBERMEYER, A. A., 1966. Mrs Reino Pott-Leendertz (1869–1965) and the Transvaal Museum Herbarium. *Bothalia* 9(1): 1–3.

OSBORNE, R., 1986. Encephalartos woodii. *Encephalartos* 5: 4–10.

PEARSE, G. E., 1956. *The Cape of Good Hope.* J. L. van Schaik. Pretoria.

PHILLIPS, E. Percy, 1930. A brief historical sketch of the development of botanical science in South Africa and the contribution of South Africa to botany. *South African Journal of Science* XXVII: 38–80.

PICARD, H. W. J., 1968. *Gentleman's Walk.* Struik. Cape Town.

PICARD, H. W. J., 1969. *Grand Parade.* Struik. Cape Town.

RAIDT, E. H. M., (ed.), 1973. *Francois Valentyn, Description of the Cape of Good Hope with matters concerning it, 1726,* part II, second series, no. 4. Van Riebeeck Society, Cape Town.

RAVENHART, R., 1971. *Cape of Good Hope, 1652–1702,* vols. I and II. A. A. Balkema. Cape Town.

REDGRAVE, J. J., 1947. *Port Elizabeth in bygone days.* Lustica Press. Wynberg.

RYCROFT, H. B., 1956. The National Botanic Gardens, Kirstenbosch. *Park Administration:* 6–11.

RYCROFT, H. B. and RYAN, R., 1980. *Kirstenbosch.* Howard Timmins. Cape Town.

SCHIRE, B. D. Centenary of the Natal Herbarium, 1882–1982. *Bothalia.* 14(2): 223–236.

SIM, T. R., 1907. *Tree planting in Natal.* Davis. Pietermaritzburg.

SPOHR, O. H., (ed.), 1967. F. Krauss, A description of Cape Town and its way of life, 1838–40. *Quarterly Bulletin of the South African Library* 21: 10.

STREY, Rudolf G., 1977. The father of Natal botany—John Medley Wood. *Natalia* 7: 43–45.

TARR, B., 1985. Natal botanic garden—an old garden with a bright future. *Veld & Flora* 71: 3–4.

THEAL, G. McC., 1897–1905. *Records of the Cape Colony, 1793–1827,* vols. ii, iii, xix, xxvii, xxviii, xxxi and xxxiv. Cape Government. Cape Town.

THOM, H. B., (ed.), 1954–57. *Journal of Jan van Riebeeck.* 3 vols, Van Riebeeck Society reprints, Cape Town.

THORP, Ernest R., 1970. *Durban botanical gardens.* Durban Parks Department. Durban.

VARLEY, D. H., (ed.), 1961. A Russian view of the Cape in 1853. *Quarterly Bulletin of the South African Library* 15: 61–62.

WILMOT, A. and CHASE, J. C., 1869. *History of the Colony of the Cape of Good Hope.* Juta & Co. Cape Town.

WOOD, J. Medley, 1899–1912. *Natal plants, Descriptions and figures of Natal indigenous plants,* 6 volumes. (Volume 1 with Maurice S. Evans). Natal Government. Durban.

Index

Supplementary index of printed material (books, journals, newspaper, etc) mentioned in the text

"Pride of Kirstenbosch", a successful horticultural hybrid bred from *Disa uniflora* and *Disa cardinalis*

Kirstenbosch — sanctuary to the splendid wild flower heritage of the Cape Floral Kingdom and a source of joy and enchantment to millions of visitors.

Six other National Botanic Gardens are situated at different centres throughout the country. Like Kirstenbosch, all these gardens are devoted to the collection, display and study of the local flora.

(Opposite, clockwise from top left) Harold Porter NBG, Betty's Bay; Karoo NBG, Worcester; Orange Free State NBG, Bloemfontein; Natal NBG, Pietermaritzburg; Lowveld NBG, Nelspruit; Witwatersrand NBG, Roodepoort/Krugersdorp.

The earliest planting at Kirstenbosch was a comprehensive collection of *Encephalartos* species. (left).

(Below) "Paintbrush flowers" *(Haemanthus coccineus)* appear each year amongst these ancient cycads splashing brilliant brushstrokes on the landscape.

The bath (below left) built by Colonel Christopher Bird in approximately 1811, was restored and became the focal point of the habitat for tree ferns and shade-loving plants. This is one of the most popular beauty spots in the garden.

(Below right) Arum lilies *(Zantedeschia aethiopica)* lend tranquillity to the moist, dappled glades.

(Above) Kirstenbosch gleams in spring when its famous annual beds are in full flower.

(Right) Mathew's Rockery, named after the first Curator, provides a good setting for a display of southern African *Aloe* species that is at its magnificent best in winter.

(Opposite page) Kirstenbosch, the garden for all people (top), combines the serenity of a lily pond with the grandeur of natural forests (bottom left) transversed by seasonal mountain streams (bottom right).

A fragrance garden (above) planted in raised beds for the benefit of the disabled, features plants with aromatic properties and unusual textures. This is linked to a braille trail (below left), where a guide-rope and annotated labels in Braille lead non-sighted visitors through the scents and sounds of the wood and marshes. A display kiosk serves as an information centre where visitors are introduced to special plant collections and interesting exhibits on the work of the gardens (below right).

Behind the scenes, a garden is a hive of activity. Enlarging the water storage dam was a vital project in the 75th anniversary year (top left). Routine maintenance of the landscaped gardens and the removal of alien vegetation (above) are ongoing activities to ensure harmonious and pleasing garden vistas (left).

Horticulture is the *raison d'etre* for any botanic garden and the staff maintains living collections of plants (right) like these beautiful but threatened *Sandersonia* and *Moraea* species (below). Comprehensive collections of Ericas (bottom left), orchids as well as rare and endangered plants are cultivated for research and *ex situ* conservation.

A major activity in international botanic gardens is the exchange of seed which involves careful collection (below) and storage (left) prior to despatch. The plant utilization section (bottom) is devoted to the propagation of indigenous plants with high horticultural potential. Several new varieties have been introduced into cultivation through this programme (inset, *Arctotis* sp.).

An annual event, not only at Kirstenbosch but at all the National Botanic Gardens, is the Plant Sale (above left), where several hundred species of native plants are available to satisfied customers (above right). A major promotional event overseas is The Chelsea Flower Show (below right) where spectacular displays, mainly of Cape flowers, win international acclaim.

A botanic garden is an invaluable educational resource and Kirstenbosch welcomes young visitors to informal classes in the garden (below) or at the Nature Study School (bottom left).

Primary school children are introduced to the wonders of the flora (below right and opposite top) while older scholars find that Kirstenbosch provides a living laboratory for ecological studies.

The Compton Herbarium, named after the second Director of the National Botanic Gardens, houses some 250,000 specimens mounted (top left) and stored in serried ranks. These provide the basis for research in all fields of botany and are consulted by scientists not only from South Africa but also from abroad.

(Top right) Seaweeds enjoy attention at the Compton Herbarium. Here, phycologists examine dried specimens and culture living collections of research material in miniature aquaria.

Outdoors, systematic botanists grow research collections. Breeding experiments are being conducted on a beautiful pink *Diascia* from the Drakensberg (above left).

A frequent visitor to this herbarium is Dr Peter Goldblatt, a world authority on the iris family (above right). Guest facilities are available at Kirstenbosch for visiting scientists.

(Opposite top) The research staff includes an entomologist who is studying the weevil that infests cycad cones and destroys developing seeds.

(Opposite) Plant pathologists investigate the causes of plant disease. Rare and endangered species are propagated by tissue culture.

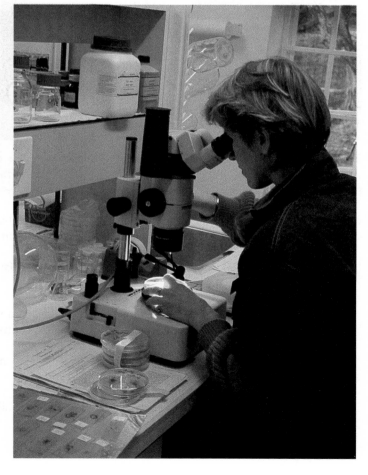

The mandate of the NBG is to "promote the conservation of, and research in connection with, southern African plants". Multi-disciplinary teamwork combines the talents of horticulturists, research scientists and educators to ensure the survival of our precious flora, such as the very rare marsh rose *Orothamnus zeyheri* (right) now in cultivation at Kirstenbosch.

CTP BOOK PRINTERS, CAPE